THE MAN WHO STAYED ALIVE is by John Creasey writing as Gordon Ashe and is in a series of which there are now over forty titles and many have been published by Corgi Books.

Born in 1908, John Creasey died in June 1973. Overall, his books have sold nearly a hundred million copies and have been translated into 28 languages.

As well as travelling extensively, he had a particular interest in politics and was the founder of *All Party Alliance*, which advocates a new system of government by the best candidates from all parties and independents. He fought in five parliamentary by-elections for the movement.

Also by JOHN CREASEY

and published by CORGI BOOKS

John Creasey

writing as Gordon Ashe

The Man Who
Stayed Alive

CORGI BOOKS
A DIVISION OF TRANSWORLD PUBLISHERS LTD

THE MAN WHO STAYED ALIVE

A CORGI BOOK 0 552 09677 6

Originally published in Great Britain
by John Long Ltd.

PRINTING HISTORY
John Long edition published 1955
Corgi edition published 1975

This book is set in Times 10pt

Corgi Books are published by Transworld Publishers, Ltd.,
Cavendish House, 57/59 Uxbridge Road, Ealing, London, W.5

Made and printed in Great Britain by
Richard Clay (The Chaucer Press), Ltd., Bungay, Suffolk.

CONTENTS

CHAPTER I

THE MAN WHO STAYED ALIVE

Two men watched as Pirran went up to the bar, unsteady on his feet, sparse, fair hair awry. The girl clinging to his right arm was responsible for that; she was a blonde, and one of the curvaceous kind, with a good complexion and a way of dressing to make sure she caught the eye. The girl clinging to his left hand was so demure that it did not look as if she could be responsible for anything. She was a brunette.

The ship rolled, and they all swayed with it.

'Whisky,' said Pirran, with the gravity of a man who was near drunkenness, ' 'n' soda—shorry!'

The roll sent him, gently, into the arms of the blonde, who helped him firmly and, when he and the ship had steadied, patted his hair again. The brunette, having let him go with the roll, took his arm again.

'And for the ladies,' went on Pirran, 'just what they require. Anyshing. Any-*th*ing.' He brought out this last triumphantly, but something in his manner suggested that he was aware of some missing factor. He searched, and found it. 'Pleashe,' he said, with great deliberation, and then nodded his head as if to make sure that he was right.

'At once, sir,' said the barman, with the precision which English barmen have, and a look which seemed to say, 'Haven't you had enough?' Whatever his scruples, he overcame them as he handled the bottles deftly.

The ship rolled.

Pirran grabbed the whisky-and-soda, a little of which spilt on to his right hand. Having secured the glass, he seemed content to let it stay where it was.

Of the two men watching from a comfortable corner in the big bar, one was large and American, and the other was medium-size and English; although many would have wondered if there were any Irish blood in him. He had a vague look of the Irish; a pair of blue eyes not only ready but eager to laugh, a full mouth which was at the beginning of

7

a smile much of the time. But this could be deceptive. When the smile vanished, the light and colour seemed to go out of his eyes, and he became a plain, undistinguished man, who could get lost in any crowd.

That was one of his great assets; a personality which could flash and sparkle, then fade into the dullness of the nondescript. He had used it to advantage throughout his life, he owed his job and his life to it.

The American was dark, with a blue-black jowl and an intense look: just then, it was almost one of disgust.

'Well, we've brought him back alive,' he said. 'I'm not so sure he was worth it.'

The Englishman said, 'Why not?'

'Look at him.'

The Englishman, whose name was Whittaker, looked steadily.

'I see what you mean, Bob,' he agreed. 'I'm not in a debating mood, but aren't you counting your chickens too early?'

'What's that?'

'Don't you have that saying on this side of the Atlantic? Counting chickens before——'

'Just make the allusion clear,' requested Bob Gann. 'He's alive, and we've done our job. We're within a hundred miles or so of New York. We'll berth in the morning soon after dawn. Nothing's gone wrong, and there's no reason why anything should go wrong now.'

Whittaker said thoughtfully: 'I hope you're right. It still worries me. No one's made any attempt to do him any harm. I don't understand it, and I don't like things I can't understand.'

'I was never sure they would try to get him,' said Gann comfortably. 'Don't worry any more, Neil. It's your night for the second watch; you can put your head down whenever you like.'

Whittaker smiled. 'Thanks,' he drawled, sounding just a little too English.

The ship rolled again.

Pirran had turned away from the bar and was making his way with portly care towards a table near the dance floor. The dancing was over and the orchestra was in bed, or should have been; only the barman, half a dozen youngsters in a curiously subdued party near the door, Whittaker and Gann, and Pirran and his attendant shapelies, were still up. It was very warm, and one of the doors was fastened back; occasionally they could hear the *swiiish* of water against the massive steel sides of the *Queen B.*

'Ooch!' exclaimed Pirran, and sat down abruptly. He would have fallen but for the help and guidance of the blonde, who saw him settled in his chair, and then patted his hair back into position. She looked at him fondly, as if she really felt affection for him, but that was hard to believe.

'Wanna go to bed,' announced Pirran, suddenly.

'That's a good idea,' the blonde said. 'Why don't we help you?'

'Would you help me, honey?' Pirran's voice was suddenly honey-sweet.

'Help you?' said honey. 'I would encourage you, Big Boy. You ever heard that story about two minds with just one idea between them?'

Pirran seemed to purr.

Whittaker, who had managed to make one whisky-and-soda last for one hour and still had a little left, tossed it down. He stood up quickly, although without any outward appearance of haste.

'Our cue,' he said to Gann. 'I'll be seeing you.' He didn't move away at once, but looked in the general direction of Pirran and the two girls. 'Bob,' he added, 'I apologise.'

'What's all this?'

'I believe this pair of cuties was born in England, so we can't refuse them passports, but we could have warned your people not to let them have visas.'

'They'll find their level in New York,' Gann said dryly.

Whittaker moved away from his corner and towards the open door. Pirran and the two lovelies were heading for another doorway which led to the big hall, the staircase and the lifts. It would take them five minutes or more to get Pirran down the stairs and into his stateroom, and possibly they would help him to undress. He had spent most of the four days they had been at sea trying to persuade one girl or another to 'visit' him; it looked as if he were about to get his own way. The puzzling thing was why they had waited until tonight.

Whittaker was on edge; the job was so nearly done, but it didn't take much to kill a man. One shot, one stab, one blow on the head—anyone could do it in a second or so.

But a killer wouldn't want to be found out, would he?

Danger came mostly from the unexpected places; and the two girls were surely too obvious.

Whittaker stepped through a narrow passage on to the deck. Although it was covered most of its length, the hiss of the sea came clearly, and a warm wind blew from the bows. He ducked into it, hurried, and then stepped through another doorway and was immediately at the head of a gangway which led to the main staterooms. He went down, swaying with the rolling of the ship, light as a cat. He reached the wide passage of the more expensive stateroom section and saw a white-clad steward sitting in his cubby-hole, reading.

'Good-night, sir.'

'Good-night.'

Whittaker moved, still quickly, until he reached a door marked *A14*. He took out a key, slid it into the lock and then pushed the door open. He was inside in a flash, and the door closed without a sound. He checked this first room, with its luxury armchairs, its luxury couch, tables, bookshelves, everything anyone could desire for comfort. He made sure that no one was in the bedroom, where the two beds looked comfortable enough for Ali Baba or even for Don Juan. The bathroom was empty, too; the whole suite was secure and ready for Augustus Pirran's sleepy head.

Why had the blonde decided to humour him tonight?

Whittaker went out and into a stateroom opposite, which was shared by him and Gann when on watch, with the steamship company's collusion. Nothing had been spared to enable them to do their job thoroughly. This room boasted a similar luxury to Pirran's, and had a little extra; there was a spy-hole at an average man's eye-level. Whittaker had to stoop in order to look across at *A14*. He heard nothing for some time, and there was just the gentle roll of the ship for company, a gentle, soothing rhythm. Then sounds came as the girls arrived, half-carrying Pirran. The blonde opened the door for him.

She helped Pirran into the stateroom, and made a good,

10

smooth job of it, as if she had been coping with drunks all her life.

The demure brunette didn't go in, but closed the door and looked as if she was quite happy to wish her girl-friend well. She walked away at once, briskly.

A man said 'Good-night' in a deep voice, and Whittaker grinned when he recognised Gann. Gann's head appeared, blocking his view; and a moment later Gann tapped sharply at the door of *A14*. He had to knock twice before he was answered, and when the door opened, he hid the blonde from Whittaker's sight.

'What do you want?' the blonde asked. Something akin to tension was in her voice.

'Wouldn't you like to know!' Gann said, and Whittaker could imagine his grin. 'Out, sweetheart.'

She began angrily:

'You go and——'

'*Out*, sweetheart,' repeated Gann, and his right shoulder moved; a moment later, the situation had altered substantially, for the blonde's back was towards Whittaker, her golden hair rippling to her shoulders, and Gann's handsome, smiling face was visible above her head. 'I'll put Papa to bed, you go and remind yourself that I've saved you from a fate worse than death.'

He patted her cheek, then went in and closed the door.

The blonde stood staring at it for some time, but she didn't speak. Her shoulders moved as if she was breathing very, very hard. Whittaker wished that he could see her face, so that he could guess at her feelings through her expression. Was she simply angry because she was disappointed of her natural prey? Had she been working up to this last night on board, deliberately holding Pirran at arm's length? Or had *she* meant to kill?

Someone meant to kill Pirran, remember.

Twice, before he had left England, Pirran had been within a hairsbreadth of death, and there was no doubt that murder had been intended. Twice, he had virtually been warned that he would not reach New York alive. In an unexpected and peculiar way, he had courage; he had not erupted into panic, but sought help.

He had looked in two places, and had found results from each. Neil Whittaker and Bob Gann had joined forces to help him.

He had put his cards on the table—or so he had said.

He wanted protection, and would buy it at a high figure. Whittaker's reputation on both sides of the Atlantic was good; he was one of the few private operators who worked in the United States as well as England, and knew many of the tricks and much of the conditions of both worlds.

For Whittaker, it meant a first-class trip to New York and back, and generous expenses. In return, on the outward journey, he had to be obsessed by one thing only: keeping Pirran alive.

For Gann . . .

Gann was F.B.I. who had been in London on official business. It had brought him into contact with Whittaker; and Pirran, as an American citizen, could claim his country's protection. Gann was authorised to give it. He and Whittaker had worked together as smoothly as Siamese twins. More than once, Whittaker had told himself they would make a wonderful team.

They didn't know why Pirran was in danger, but he had convinced them that he was.

It was a matter of professional pride to each that their charge should reach New York alive, but as the voyage had progressed, each man had come to like Pirran less and less. Instead of making Whittaker worry less, it made him worry more; it would be easier to get slack over a man one didn't like.

Whittaker went out of the stateroom when the blonde had moved towards the main hall. She walked briskly, and didn't look behind her; obviously she had no idea that she was being followed. Whittaker found himself smiling in recollection. Gann had done a smooth job; from the first moment of meeting, it had been obvious that he and Gann would get along.

Now the partnership was nearly over; and in some ways that was a pity.

It was odd that in four days you could get to know a man so well that it was possible to regard him as an old friend; to be sure that whatever happened in the future, you would keep in touch. He liked Gann for a number of reasons, and he was looking forward to visiting his home, in a place called Scarsdale; to meeting his wife, and meeting his two

12

children. He would recognise them from colour photographs which Gann carried, and which had been on the locker of the double cabin which they shared.

If the photograph of Mrs. Gann was a fair likeness, it made Gann a lucky man. She was the kind of woman who made any man look twice. Whittaker had studied the picture several times, and felt almost as if he knew her.

The children looked happy and healthy.

Everything considered, Gann's family made a good advertisement for marriage.

Whittaker watched the blonde go down a flight of stairs towards the cabins which lacked the luxury of those near *A14*. She walked well. She had behaved well enough after the rebuff, he supposed. He wished he had been able to see her expression, but imagination could fill in a great many gaps. Gann would look after everything that mattered until it was time for him, Whittaker, to take over; he would wake, because he could wake whenever he wanted. That wasn't nature's gift, but a matter of training.

The blonde had vanished. Even now, it was easy to dwell upon her figure.

Whittaker moved towards a passage at the other side of the big hall, where he and Gann had their sleeping cabin. It was close enough to *A14* to be handy, not so near that anyone's suspicions were likely to be aroused. He was reflecting that until tonight there had not seemed the slightest reason for fears for Pirran; nothing at all had happened to cause alarm. Pirran had not betrayed any particular uneasiness, except that tendency to get drunk early in an evening, and to stay that way until he went to bed; he was always in bed very late.

Frightened men often feared sleep.

Anyhow, the man would hardly pay good money, and a lot of it, for protection from an imaginary danger.

Whittaker yawned.

It was a little before two o'clock. He decided to go and relieve Gann at four. By six, the ship would be astir with that curious and contagious excitement which seemed to affect everyone, new travellers and seasoned ones, when they were within sight of the New York skyline.

If it was daylight, they would be able to see the coast of Long Island even now. Would a turn round the deck be a good thing, or . . .

He yawned again, decided 'no' and went into his cabin—and stopped before closing the door. There was the faint drone of the engines and the creaking of the sides of the ship, all the familiar noises; and there was one which wasn't familiar in here; the sound of someone breathing. He was quite sure of that beyond any possibility of a mistake. He was outlined against the light in the passage, a clear silhouette; and if danger came leaping, an easy target.

He heard just that breathing; saw no danger.

He kept the door half-open, and switched on a light. The breathing continued, uninterrupted. He could see the head of one bed, and only the side of another. The first bed was empty. On the other, just in sight, was a woman's hand, pale, slender, with long, well-shaped finger-nails varnished a bright red.

Whittaker moved so that he could see more.

She lay in his bunk, under the bedclothes, dark hair vivid against the pillow, pretty face turned towards him, nice, tanned shoulders bare. She seemed to be asleep.

She was the brunette who had been so demure with Pirran.

*   *   *

It was utterly unexpected; so much so that for a moment it put him off his guard.

But not for long.

CHAPTER II

SLEEPING BEAUTY

ONCE he had recovered from the shock, Whittaker leaned back and looked both ways along the passage. No one was in sight, and there were only the familiar, friendly noises of the ship. He stepped into the room and closed and locked the door. By that time he had completely recovered from the effect of the first surprise, his heart was back to normal, and a smile played about the corners of his lips.

14

Yet he made a mistake. It was a grave one; and in some ways it was deadly.

He was not aware of it, then.

He stepped towards the girl, who lay so still and who looked so demure, even in sleep. She was a pretty little poppet, and he remembered that when she had been sun-bathing on the boat-deck, and dancing in a gown which the conventional would call *décolleté*, she had attracted the gaze of men for all the obvious reasons. There was nothing of the blonde's sensuousness; she was 'nice'.

It was easy to believe that she was asleep, and not pretending. He watched her for several seconds, but she didn't stir.

'Sweetheart,' he said at last, 'it won't work.'

She still didn't move.

'Give it up,' he said.

He spoke very quietly, watching her closely. Her dark eyelashes curled to her cheeks, and her eyes didn't twitch. She still wore her make-up. For a split second, he wondered if she was breathing at all, and because the thought of death in such sweet beauty was hideous, his heart gave a sudden jump.

He saw her lips move, slightly.

'Beautiful,' he said, more loudly, 'this was one of your big mistakes.'

She gave no sign that she had heard him.

The truth was—it was no excuse, and afterwards he never used it as one—that the sight of her intrigued him, especially the rounded, golden smoothness of her shoulders. There was nothing remarkable about that, for he was all man. It was as if she had just slipped out of her clothes and climbed into his bed and dropped, exhausted, into sleep. Her dressing-gown and some nylon flimsies were on a chair, a pair of heel-less slippers on the floor beneath it. She was really something to see, and it wouldn't be difficult to have fun. But that wasn't the idea; not his, anyhow. The hard thing to believe was that it was hers. He knew how easy it was to be taken in by a woman, knew that her friend the blonde wouldn't have surprised him as this girl did, and yet——

'Come on, wake up!' he said, more firmly, and gripped her shoulder.

Her flesh was warm and soft, of course, but she didn't

15

show that she heard or felt him. Except where his movements made her, she didn't move at all. Suddenly, he felt mad at her, but he didn't let that affect him. He studied her closely, his thoughts racing. Then he slapped her face, not hard but sharply, and suddenly pulled the sheet down, ready to slide his arms beneath her, and lift her off the bed.

He did nothing of the kind; just stood still.

She wasn't wearing a stitch of clothing.

He swallowed hard. This was more than the wine of temptation; this was the champagne. She was beautifully formed, with a small waist and hips slim for a woman, long slender legs. There were the white marks where her bikini kept the sun off her skin, and this soft whiteness had its own peculiar kind of attractiveness. He felt his heart thumping and his pulse beating, as he looked down at her demure face and her relaxed body. It was easy to forget the job he was here to do, and that she was undoubtedly here to stop him from doing it. He stood staring down for a few seconds; they could not have been more than a few seconds, although in one dreadful way they were fateful ones. Even when his tension relaxed, he didn't even begin to dream of the awfulness of his mistake.

Then another smile broke through the tautness of his eyes and his expression.

'Very nice,' he said. 'Now I wonder what this is all about.' But he knew what it was about, and just why she was here. Could anyone imagine him going out of the cabin, now? Most people would think she would keep him in here much more securely than any locked door.

She wouldn't keep *him*.

He picked up a nylon stocking, gossamer thin but strong, held it between his hands, and then placed it on the pillow above her head, stretched tautly. Then with a swift movement he pulled it beneath her head, and for the first time her eyes opened, her body moved.

'Wha . . .' she began.

'We'll talk later, sweetheart,' Whittaker said, and before she realised what he was going to do, he pulled the stocking round her face and knotted it over her lips. She was too shocked at first to struggle or try to speak, and when he had finished she couldn't utter a word. With her rounded eyes wider open and her face flushed from shock, she looked

16

even lovelier. She had a lot that the blonde hadn't, and Whittaker found himself wondering what made her play this kind of game.

She was some mother's daughter; and grief.

'I won't keep you long,' he said, and lifting her bodily, carried her to a hanging cupboard in the corner, and thrust her inside. By then she was kicking, but her toes suffered more than his shin. He unhooked a coat from a hanger, held her inside the cupboard with one hand and draped the coat round her with the other.

'Nice and respectable, aren't we?' he asked, and closed and locked the door.

She hadn't a chance to get out, by herself.

She might get the stocking off, but she wasn't likely to want to attract attention by shouting. She would wait for him.

Now his grin faded; grimness replaced it, as if he had some prevision of horror. He went towards the door swiftly, stepped into the passage and closed the door and locked it in one moment. He moved swiftly now, ignoring the gentle roll of the ship and all the sounds. He felt a sudden, desperate need for haste now that the girl was no longer here to mesmerise him. A steward coming along the passage from the hall stopped abruptly at the sight of him.

'Goo—good-night, sir.'

' 'Night,' said Whittaker, brusquely.

He sped across the silent hall towards stateroom *A14*; as he reached it his key, a pass-key Gann had obtained, slid into his hand, and the cold metal was sharp against his sweating palm. He slid the key into the lock, turned it and opened the door—and everything he did was charged with that fear, and with the sickening realisation of the possibility of being too late.

He had taken too much time with the girl. Of course he had; he had even fooled himself. Anyone who knew him would know that he would see through the ruse, would expect him to leave the girl there, and hurry to Gann. They had calculated that she would delay him for a little while; that was all.

And they had.

He felt a fierce anger with himself, as well as fear. For a split second he thought that his fears had been groundless,

17

that Gann was still there, and therefore Pirran was safe.

Then, Whittaker saw part of the horror.

Gann *was* still here; but on macabre guard, sitting in a chair which faced the door of the bedroom. He was fully dressed. Profile towards Whittaker, he had never looked more arrestingly handsome—if only one could forget the back of his head.

Standing there with the open door swinging gently behind him, Whittaker knew then that he could never forget, and never forgive himself for losing time. Gann's skull might have been crushed by one blow or a dozen. Blood was on the back of Gann's coat, on the back of the chair, on the pale-coloured carpet; the bright glistening red of newly-spilt blood. There wasn't a chance that he was alive.

His right arm hung limp over the side of his chair.

Hardly aware of what he was doing, Whittaker closed the door and moved forward, stretching out for Gann's hand. It was easier to look at him from the front—one could remember but not see the full horror of what had happened. The fingers felt warm. Whittaker's forefinger pressed gently, but there was no pulse beat, no hint of life. He lowered the hand gently, but the roll of the ship made it sway to and fro. Whittaker turned away, teeth gritting. While he had been looking at the girl, this . . .

He made himself go towards the bedroom door. It was closed. He hesitated outside it for a second, then grasped the handle and flung it open, quite prepared to see that this room was a shambles, too, and his mission an utter failure.

Pirran lay sleeping. *Sleeping*. His mouth was open in a fish-like pose. He feared the sun as he had seemed to fear the night, and his face was pale and flabby. He was snoring faintly, his lips quivering with the intake of breath. He wasn't undressed, but his shoes were off, and his black bow-tie had been ripped from his collar; the white dress-shirt gaped at the front, showing that Augustus Pirran was a flabby, hairless individual. Lying there, he looked like a fish in black and white, a spiteful caricature of a man.

He was alive.

Not only that; it looked as if he had come straight in here, kicked off his own shoes and wrenched open his own neck-band, and dropped down, exhausted. The blonde had probably helped him.

18

The blonde, remember. Only a few seconds passed while Whittaker stood there motionless, but they were seconds he would not want to live through again. They scorched themselves into his mind like words of a branding iron. He might have stopped this. If he had left the brunette on the bed, not trying to make her move, he might have reached Gann in time to save his life.

There was no way of being certain; there would always be the dread.

Now, he must act. There was a killer to find.

Whittaker looked back at the door. It had closed with the motion of the ship, but swung open again. No sound came. He didn't realise that he had taken it from his case, but found himself drawing at a lighted cigarette. Then he looked about the bedroom, taking stock of everything in sight.

The chaos didn't really surprise him, except for one thing; the search had been done so quickly.

Drawers stuck out of the dressing-chest, handkerchiefs, socks, ties, all the oddments a man would take round with him, were in jumbled heaps. The floor was littered. A tin of talcum powder, faintly-scented, lay on the carpet with a trail of powder showing upon the spot where it had fallen. Suitcases had been pulled from beneath the bed, and opened, but all of these seemed empty. A hide brief-case lay on a chair, open.

Whittaker picked it up; it was empty, too.

They had moved fast. In fact, fast was hardly the word for it. Need he blame himself so bitterly? How long had he been gone? Allow two minutes, at most, from the time he had turned into the passage and followed the blonde; well, say three to the time when he had opened his own cabin door. Then there had been the pause, when he had heard the breathing. A minute? It had seemed longer, but he doubted whether it had been as long; in moments of tension, time seemed to stand still. Then switching on the light, seeing the girl, staring at her, moving towards her. . . .

How *long*?

There was no way of telling, but he had to accept one thing; he hadn't really hurried. That blame was fully deserved. God forgive him, he had been amused. For the few vital minutes, he had felt quite sure that this was the first move in the game of seek-and-kill with Pirran, but his mind hadn't worked fast enough or in the right direction. Something had happened to make the search of this room a sudden, vital need. Something had happened to make Bob Gann's murder imperative.

Had Bob made some discovery dangerous to his killer?

Why leave *Pirran* alive?—the man who was to have been killed. Had there been any change in their plans? Any reason to kill Gann and leave Pirran alive? No one could possibly have mistaken one man for the other, the killer had known whom he was killing.

They'd tried to make sure that the way was clear, the dark girl's job had simply been to make sure that he didn't come back—*in time*.

Well, she had a tongue. He could picture those inviting golden shoulders, the sheet lying on her so lightly; it had been done with the genius of a man who knew men, knew that he wasn't likely to leave her at once.

Or a woman who knew them.

How long had he been away?

He went back to the drawing-room of *A14*, where everything except the back of Bob Gann's head looked normal. The blood sinking in the carpet had spread wider, and as he entered the room he heard a light splash.

He made himself look into Gann's handsome face. As he did so, other faces seemed to superimpose themselves on to the dead man's. He could picture Gann's children in the colour photograph, but they were vague and misty. Not so Gann's wife; he saw her face as clearly as in the photograph on Gann's locker; every feature, every line, the fine eyes, the lips puckering into the beginning of a smile.

Mrs. Gann.

Widow Gann.

Whittaker wrenched his thoughts away. He knew that he was suffering from shock, that he was still losing precious time. *Think*.

Gann had been quite sure of himself. Pirran was in the bedroom; probably Pirran had been lying on the bed when he had entered. Picture the scene; the blonde helping Pirran to bed, and before she could make a job of it, having to open the door to Gann. Gann had sent her marching, gone in, probably found Pirran lying there in a drunken stupor. He had pulled the chair up and sat down for his vigil. To

Gann, it must have seemed a mere formality, and yet someone had crept into this room, approached him without a sound, and struck with brutish fury.

He had meant to kill. There had been no time for anyone to wait until Gann dozed. That was the heart of the puzzle. How had it been done in the time? Gann had been wide awake, and on top of his job, had even cut down on his drinks because he had the job to do. He had been in a good humour, and cold stone sober; yet someone had got in, crept up on him, and given him no chance at all.

Whittaker looked about the room. He was wondering whether he could have made an even worse mistake; whether there was anywhere in this outer room for a man or woman to hide. The unbelievable thing was that anyone could creep up on Gann while he was wide awake. You didn't become a top man of the F.B.I. by letting yourself go deaf. Gann could have been drugged, but how? Thoughts came swiftly enough now. Poison in a drink meant help from the bar-keeper, and few things were less likely. In cigarettes? It was just possible. If Gann had lost consciousness then, through drugs, how long ago had he taken the stuff? And how was it they had taken effect at the vital moment?

There was no way of telling; and Whittaker believed that drugs were out.

Then how . . . ?

He went over everything he had done, and felt a little better; less tense and vicious with himself. There was nowhere here for a man or woman to hide, except places where he had looked. The only door led into the passage. The bedroom porthole was closed and the screw fastenings very tight.

He went to the passage door, and examined the lock on the inside, bending down and breathing on the shiny chromium. Finger-prints showed up—but even as he did it, he recognised that as a waste of time, there must inevitably be a lot of finger-prints, and he had no facilities to check them. The outside of the door would show scratches if the lock had been picked, and he began to open the door.

He closed it again.

He did not believe it possible for anyone to lock or unlock a door with a pick-lock without Gann hearing. A pass-key or an ordinary key must have been used. It wasn't difficult to get a key; one could 'borrow' one, make a soap impression and have a duplicate made in a matter of an hour or so, if one came prepared; and the certain thing was that the murderer had come prepared. An oiled key would make little noise, and the hinges were silent when he moved them. The simple truth was that Gann had sat there feeling absolutely secure, convinced that no one could get into the room without him hearing. Over-confidence could be deadly, and now that he looked back, he could bring him self to believe that Gann might have the fault.

Well, he, Whittaker, was cured of it.

He wished he could have seen the blonde's face.

He made another quick search of the room, but found nothing that helped. He looked in the brief-case again, and satisfied himself that it was empty. One room in chaos and the other tidy suggested that the murderers had found what they had come for in the case; unless they had been scared off. That wasn't likely. They had come to rob Pirran, remember, not to kill him; yet the original threat had been to kill.

When he had been entirely at their mercy, they had let him live.

It was time to talk to the girl in his cabin.

Time to make some move, anyway.

Whittaker listened at the door, made sure that no one was approaching, and went into the passage. He stepped into the big room across the way, went to a cupboard, poured himself a whisky and tossed it down. He lit another cigarette, and as he stared at the glowing tip it looked like the back of Bob Gann's head.

He opened the door again and this time turned towards the blonde's cabin. He knew its number, he had seen her come out of it. She shared the cabin with the brunette. He reached the door, seeing the light on in a steward's cubbyhole, but having no need to pass it; as far as he knew, he was not seen.

But one could never be sure, on board ship. Doors had more eyes and more ears than anywhere else. Doors were so often latched, and there were so many of them. A man or woman could open one and glance out and then withdraw into the room, unseen and unheard—yet a deadly witness. The stewards were trained to move quietly and to

22

show absolute discretion; but they had alert ears and sharp eyes.

There was no absolute safety on board; no way of being sure that he could move anywhere without being observed.

Tonight, Whittaker was more edgy than he had ever been.

Standing at the cabin door, he felt his heart at its old, palpitating tricks.

What would he find here?

CHAPTER III

TWO . . . THREE

THERE was no light on inside the cabin, but that meant nothing. There was no sound but the sounds which belonged to a ship at sea. The light from the passage cast Whittaker's shadow into the cabin, and it wouldn't help to stay outside. He went in quickly and closed the door without a sound. Then he groped for the light switch, but it wasn't in the position of the switch in his cabin, and he touched only the smooth wall.

He let his arm fall.

There was no sound of breathing, nothing here to give him cause for alarm.

He drew on his cigarette, and it made a pink glow about the tip of his nose; just a glimmer in the blackness. He took out his lighter, but before flicking it on, stood in the silence, listening, in spite of his certainty that there was no sound of breathing.

The dead did not breathe, and he was prepared to believe that anything could have happened in this cabin; anywhere on board.

He flicked the lighter.

The light was dim but, in the first moment, bright enough to dazzle him. He narrowed his eyes against it. Then he could see the glow, and the foot of the bed, the mirror reflecting the light and his own sinister looming figure; all the things he would expect to see, nothing to add to the night's horror.

The beds seemed empty.

He made out the shape of the light switch, and pressed down.

The beds *were* empty.

One was rumpled, as if someone had been sitting on it, and that was more than a guess. The blonde wasn't as tidy as the brunette. On the floor was a pair of pale nylon stockings, filmy things dropped casually as the woman had taken them off her slim legs. On the bed was a bra, a pair of panties, which looked too fragile for words, and a belt which hardly warranted the name belt. All of these were pink. Over a chair was the rose-coloured evening gown the blonde had worn that night. On her, it had seemed almost part of her, a living thing; but here it was, a lifeless piece of satin, with a few tawdry, glittering pieces sewn on to it. It looked too limp to have belonged to a woman so full of vitality.

Where was she?

If she had been in the bathroom, he would surely have heard some sound of movement. He heard none at all. He strained his ears, conscious of the slight creaking sound that the ship made, and then he stiffened, becoming slowly aware of another sound, and one which made him shiver.

He didn't like shivering for reasons of that kind. It was *drip-drip-drip*. He had noticed it before, but it was only now that he was wondering where the blonde had gone did he connect it with that one *drop* from the back of Gann's chair.

The door of the bathroom was closed.

It wasn't a full bathroom, just a toilet with a cubicle for a shower. This cabin was identical with that which he and Gann had shared, except that everything was the other way round. Once he realised that, he could find his way about.

Drip-drip-drip.

There was no other sound, and that made the dripping noise seem louder, and it also made Whittaker's breath come in shorter, sharper measure. There was nothing at all in this night's happenings that he liked, and he was prepared to believe the worst of everything.

Drip. . . .

The truth was that he was living on the edge of his nerves. He had seen a thing which he had not believed possible; and imagining others which might never happen. He was screwing himself up to face something which might be like a figment in a nightmare. In fact, he felt much as he would if this were a nightmare. He felt stiff and cold, and suspected that if he opened his mouth to scream, no sound would come.

Standing here, fighting for complete calm, he knew that it would be easy to go out of the cabin and turn his back on whatever was here. But once he did that he would be finished. He would never be able to take on a job again, would be forever mocked by his own cowardice.

He dropped the latch of the passage door, to make sure that no one could get in, then advanced towards the shower door. He touched the handle very lightly, pushed it down, and eased the door open. As he did so, he realised that the ship had stopped rolling; there was hardly any movement at all.

He felt better, now that he was on the move.

He looked inside the cubicle.

He should not have been surprised, and yet what he saw kicked him so hard that at first he could not move. Here was all the nightmare horror that he had feared.

The blonde was there, on the floor, with the plastic curtain which separated the shower from the rest of the compartment drawn back. Water swayed gently about the huddled body, lapping at creamy legs and creamy arms, covering the scarlet nails of the right hand.

She had died as Gann had died, and the water against white tiles was tinged a soft and lovely pink.

*　　*　　*

Whittaker stepped back into the cabin and eased his collar, which felt tight enough to choke him. It was that nightmare world. He did not even remember the way he had talked to Gann, up in the bar while watching Pirran and his two ladies for the night. All that was in the past—like life for Gann and for the blonde. Her face was hidden from him, and he still could not see whether there was any expression on it. The temptation to turn his back on this new horror was almost too strong to resist, and he had to make a conscious fight against it. If he turned away, what could he hope to win? He was known to share Gann's room and to be working with him; he would escape nothing,

25

and might increase the risk of being suspected.

He was there, with a job to do.

Two jobs.

First, save Pirran's life. Second, find out who had killed Gann and the girl who now lay dead.

He looked about the cabin with steady eye, on top of his job now. There was nothing to suggest that it had been searched. The girl had come in, sat on the side of the bed, stripped, gone for the shower and, under the sound of the hissing water, heard nothing of the approach of the killer. It was much easier to understand that than to understand how Gann had been taken by surprise.

Whittaker moved to the dressing-chest, opened it and looked through everything he could find. Work gave him needed calmness. He didn't find much, but a passport with the blonde's photograph told him that her name was Maisie Gregson, that she had blue eyes, fair hair, that she was five feet six in height, and that she lived at Linton Court, Bayswater, London. The other passport gave the same kind of skeleton story. The brunette was Olive Johns; she had grey eyes, dark hair, and was five feet five in height; there were a few details he could have supplied, missing from the document. She lived at Linton Court, Bayswater, London. So presumably they shared a flat.

They *had* shared. . . .

Whittaker put the passports away.

In an envelope he found a vaccination certificate, some traveller's cheques, and odd papers, and a letter from the Lamprey Hotel, Broadway at 61st Street, confirming a booking for an apartment with a bedroom and a living-room for Miss Maisie Gregson, at a rent of $27·50 a week.

Not exactly luxury.

Whittaker kept the letter, but left everything else.

He went slowly to the door, listened again, and then stepped out.

A steward turned the corner, taking Whittaker completely by surprise. It was an indication of his cool nerve that he showed no sign of jumpiness and felt very little. He did not even need to keep a poker-face, but was quite natural and relaxed.

The steward also kept a completely straight face, as stewards do. He was a plump man, going bald—especially

26

at the front of his head: it gave him an intellectual appearance which was probably misleading. His eyes looked tired and his wrinkled lids drooped. There was no shadow of doubt that he knew which room Whittaker had come from, and it was at least probable that he had seen others come from there during the voyage. He inclined his head with the courtliness of an old hand at the game.

'Good-night, sir.'

'Good-night.'

They passed. Whittaker didn't slacken his pace, but once the man was behind him, found that his heart was outpacing itself. In the morning the blonde would be found, and the steward would report exactly what he had seen. So in the morning, unless he took sharp, evasive action, there would be a hue and cry for him. Before, he had simply been an obvious man to question because he knew Gann. Now, he had been in a position to have committed two murders, and that wasn't a thing that anyone could laugh off.

Was he being framed?

He jibbed at the thought, and quickened his pace.

It was as if his heart were a puffing engine, forcing him to go faster and faster, making his legs move like pistons. He knew exactly what he feared, and the encounter with the steward had put it into clearer perspective. It was useless to tell himself that a third could not have happened, that two murders for one night were more than enough; he was frightened by the possibility that when he reached his own cabin, he would find the brunette dead.

Could that third horror lie in wait for him?

He took the steps up towards the hall three at a time, turned the bend in them—and saw the man's legs, the brightly polished brown shoes, the socks with red, white and blue rings round them. One moment there were just the stairs—the next the legs, and the shoes and socks.

At first Whittaker stood aside to let the other pass. His thoughts were of the brunette and the possibility that she was dead in his cabin. If she were, and if anyone else found her, then he would probably never save his neck—and saving it was an overpowering necessity.

Then, there were the man's feet. Unmoving.

From the moment he first saw them to the moment when he began to understand, only a few seconds passed. Whittaker had moved to one side, and was now on a step near the corner, but the other man hadn't moved.

He did move, suddenly, savagely.

Whittaker had no time to look further, and to see what the man's face was like. In that few seconds of grace, he sensed what was coming, and flung his arms upwards, putting his hands across his head. The first blow from the stranger smashed down with agonising force. Whittaker thought that the fingers were broken; he knew that they had saved his skull from being smashed in like a shell.

The man grunted, and was ready to strike again.

Whittaker flung himself forward. The second blow missed his head and his hands and fell, limply, on to the small of his back. The force of his own blow made the attacker lurch forward, and then the one thing Whittaker hoped for happened. The man went sprawling, tossed over Whittaker's back.

Whittaker straightened up, but could hardly keep his feet. He had stopped thinking now, had only the animal instinct to save himself.

The upwards movement sent the attacker hurtling through the air and crashing to the side of the staircase. He hit it with a crunching kind of thud and fell to the floor like a sack. Whittaker knew then that the danger had gone, but that was his only thought. His hands were afire, and in spite of their protection, his head felt as if it had been savagely battered. He managed to turn so that he was sitting on the stairs, head in his hands, staring through his fingers at the crumpled body of his assailant.

The man lay quite still, in an oddly twisted position.

Whittaker watched him, stupidly. The ache in his own head, the horror of all that had happened, combined to make him feel just numbed. He had been very near death. The savagery of the blows had been a kind that could crush a man's skull—as Gann's had been crushed, as well as the blonde's. His fingers had saved him; that and the fact that he had been going forward, so that a little of the force of the blow had been wasted.

Get that: *he* had nearly been the third victim. What was happening? Had some madman started to kill . . .?

This was death by design: Gann, him, the blonde. But he was alive, and the would-be-killer was lying there.

Whittaker noticed the peculiar way the man's neck was bent, but couldn't think why. He began to work his fingers about, cautiously, and they hurt a little less. There was a spot of pain in the small of his back, but nothing that mattered. He began to think more rationally and, with thinking, began to feel also a sense of triumph at his own escape. First Gann, then Maisie Gregson, had died from a savage blow on the back of the head, and he had saved himself by a sub-conscious movement and a lot of luck.

He had always believed in his lucky star.

He had a sense of anti-climax as he stared at the man, who was dressed in a navy-blue suit, whose face was turned towards the wall, whose ringed socks were clearly visible because of the way his trousers had hitched up as he had fallen. Near him was a bludgeon, spiked and bloody. He would soon come round, and when he came round, he would talk. He would have to.

Whittaker gulped.

He took his hands from his head, and looked harder at the unconscious man.

'No,' he said, huskily. 'No.'

He got up, and found it necessary to cling to the hand rail; his head seemed to go up and down, as if the ship had started rolling again. It hadn't. He went down two steps, one at a time, and felt as if he would never again be able to move freely. He stared without shifting his gaze, and what he saw made him lick his lips, and then say again:

'No.'

Yet in his bones he knew what he feared was true. The man had struck the walnut panelling of the staircase with such force that he had broken his neck. That was why his head was in such an odd position.

Whittaker made himself go down on one knee, felt for the pulse, and knew that he was right.

He straightened up.

'One, two, three,' he said, stupidly. 'One, two, three—four.'

He clenched his teeth.

If he were going to lose his head, this would be the time. Do the wrong thing now, and he was finished. If he were actually seen by the side of a dead man, what would words and explanations do to help? Gann; the girl; this brute. It

29

was as bad as being caught red-handed, and yet—here was
the nightmare. He couldn't make himself move; he felt as
if his joints were all locked; arms, legs, hands, mouth.
There were limits to what a man could take, and he had
been severely shocked twice tonight, had not really recovered from the first one.

He must move.

He tried to make himself, but was still in that locked
position.

Then, as if from a long way off, he heard sounds; footsteps. Someone was coming towards the stairs from the hall.
Whittaker moved away from them, made a desperate effort,
and broke through the paralysis. Once able to move, he
went down quickly, and made very little sound. He dared not
stop, or soothe his swelling head. He couldn't stop his heart
from thumping, either. He reached the next deck, when he
heard the footsteps stop, and heard a sharp exclamation.
He moved towards the staircase on the other side, and
went up them. At least the nightmare was past. Was it?
That other girl . . .

A man shouted something which sounded like, 'Steward!'
The word carried the ring of panic.

Whittaker reached the main hall from the other staircase
several minutes later. He was outwardly quite normal, and
inwardly a great deal better, but there was one dreaded
thing on his mind; fear of finding the brunette dead, too.
He tried to keep the thought out of his mind, but it stayed
there, immovable. He saw other people without any feeling
of dismay or fear—as if sure that he would not be in danger
until he had seen the girl.

He would not allow himself to move too quickly. By now,
men were hurrying towards the staircase. He recognised the
ship's doctor, and the purser, a small man and a big one.
There were also several passengers, three of them fully-
dressed, two in dressing-gowns. Men were whispering.
Three white-coated stewards had appeared as if from
nowhere, and were taking up a position as of guard at the
head of the stairs; there would be others below.

A man with a shock of red hair, and wearing a green
dressing-gown, said to Whittaker:

'Do you know what's happened?' He sounded scared.

'Afraid I don't.' Whittaker was pleased with himself; his voice could not have been steadier or more casual.

'A man's *dead.*'

'Dead?' echoed Whittaker, as if he lived in a world which knew not death. 'That's pretty ugly. *Dead?*' he repeated. 'But how . . .'

'I'm told it's a broken neck.'

'Extraordinary thing,' observed Whittaker, and looked towards the stewards. 'They seem to have everything under control, though. Nothing we can do, is there?' He mustn't be too casual.

'Well—well, I suppose not,' said the red-haired man. 'As you say, extraordinary.' He blinked at the stewards, and looked as if he dared venture further, so that he could get first-hand evidence. Instead, he stood where he was, clutching the dressing-gown about him.

Whittaker reached his own passage. There was just the one sense of fear; of what he might find.

Two more stewards and a nurse were coming along, all walking briskly, all looking as if they had been woken from a deep sleep. They hardly noticed Whittaker, but that was not remarkable, in view of that strange ability to lose himself even among a small group of people. There was a quickness in the men's step which told of sensation waiting for them. A kind of eagerness. Whittaker had no eagerness, only the dread of what might be waiting for him.

He heard someone in the passage behind him, and glanced over his shoulder. There was nothing nervous in his manner or his emotions; fear of what would happen if he were suspected was driven away by the all-pervading dread. He could picture the girl as she had lain there when he had first entered his cabin; how she had looked when he had pulled the bedclothes down.

Perfection.

Beauty.

Vital, throbbing life.

The man behind Whittaker was the man in the green dressing-gown. He turned into a room three removed from Whittaker's, and the door slammed.

Whittaker turned to his own door, and touched the handle, but for a moment didn't turn it. He felt almost sure what he would find, and he dreaded the moment of discovery. He wanted time to get away from other people, to put both time and distance away from the horror that had happened tonight. He had rubbed shoulders with violence all of his life, but never a holocaust like this. It was worse because of what might wait behind this door. He forgot that he had been seen coming out of dead Maisie's room; and later, near the hall after the man had been found dead; that he would be known as a friend of Gann's. But he began to remember these; and to remind himself that he had been seen coming from the passage where *A14* was situated.

Now if a dead woman were found in his own cabin. . . .

He flung the door open, let it bang back, and waited for a second, to make sure that no one was there. His heart was banging uncontrollably.

Unless they hid in the shower, no one was.

He stepped in, closed and locked the door, and went to the wardrobe cupboard. He felt choked. His hands were clammy, yet cold. It was a full minute before he could bring himself to open that door. When he did, it was with a savage movement and that fear amounting almost to conviction that the brunette would be dead.

She wasn't there.

*   *   *

His relief was so great that he felt sick. He clutched the side of the door, swaying; and stared about him. He could see every corner, and the girl wasn't here.

Unsteadily, he turned to the room.

He was sweating freely and he felt physical nausea. He had been so positive in his own mind that it was almost impossible to accept the truth.

Here *was* the truth.

Whatever had happened to the brunette, she wasn't in here, dead.

Not like the blonde.

Not like Bob Gann.

'Take it easy,' Whittaker said to himself. 'Just take it easy.' His head was swimming, but he didn't think that would last for long.

Now if only he were given a little time, he might stand a chance to cover up his own traces, and be free to get on the trail of the killer.

Just give him time.

CHAPTER IV

SLEEPING PARTNER

WHITTAKER sat smoking and looking across at the cupboard. The cabin was quiet. He made himself sit there, within hand's distance of whisky, but keeping his hand still. His head was much better; his fingers were sore, that was all.

He had been granted a little time. Not enough, yet, but already he was better able to cope.

He heard people moving along the passage, several of them at a time, and was quite sure that the body of the dead man was being carried along towards the ship's mortuary. He heard the shuffling footsteps, and the way a man said 'Careful' as if it could matter whether the dead man knocked against the wall or not. Reality was back; he could think logically, the dread had quite gone.

The sounds faded into the distance. The ship creaked a little.

Whittaker stubbed out his cigarette and then helped himself to a whisky-and-soda; a weak one. He was able to smile wryly. The great ship was very steady, not at all as it had been when Pirran had stumbled across the dance floor, supported by the brunette and the now dead blonde.

It was a little after three o'clock.

Whittaker didn't try to force his thoughts into any particular channels—just let them drift. That way, the unimportant ones would vanish of their own accord, the vital ones show up. In fact, the process didn't take long; and what was left gave him plenty to worry about.

Fact one, Gann was dead and Pirran was alive.

That mattered most and hurt most. Reason told Whittaker that no matter how quickly he had left his cabin, he would have reached *A14* too late; but reason and logic

33

didn't help. He *might* have been in time. He couldn't blame himself, even remotely, for Maisie Gregson's death, but . . . he couldn't forget the steward with his knowing nod which had been almost a wink, and the inescapable fact that this man had seen Whittaker come out of the cabin where, sooner or later, the dead girl would be found.

The inevitable consequence was obvious suspicion of murder. It could be taken a step further; a charge of murder on the high seas.

Whittaker sat very still.

The whisky did him good, warming him where he had felt cold. He could think of his own danger now, and that was a healthy sign. Half an hour ago he had scared himself because he had wanted to turn his back on the past and the future, and to run. Now, he wouldn't run away from anything—but he might run into even more trouble.

While he was on board, there was so much to do; but how long dare he stay? How long would it be before he was questioned, perhaps detained?

There were a thousand things to do, remember. So many people to see.

Augustus Pirran, for one; try to find out more from him, and never mind the fact that Pirran was paying him. He must make Pirran talk more freely, soon.

There was another must.

Find the brunette, so demure Olive Johns, and make her talk, too. She would know plenty, and she should be easy to scare.

Work *fast*.

But—dare he stay on board? Wouldn't the hunt be up for him? There were three ways in which he could be associated with the murders, and one of the three was certain to make him vulnerable.

Could he get off, even if he wanted to? This was the trouble; indecision. What was the wise thing to do?

Remember . . . Gann was dead and Pirran was alive. If Pirran had ever been in danger of murder, it had been tonight; surely danger to him could be forgotten now; there was no need to think of staying simply out of loyalty to Pirran. Gann's death had changed all that, hadn't it?

Face *facts*.

Soon, the ship's officials would be questioning him, and

once that started they were likely to keep it up. The pressure might not be hard at the first questioning, but once that steward named him or the man by the stairs, then they would start hotting it up.

There was no shadow of doubt: he ought to get ashore.

But if he did, what could he do? He knew New York as well as most people, but wouldn't be able to use his normal contacts; in fact, once he had left the ship, suspicion of him would turn into virtual certainty. There was no real safety ashore.

What alternative was there? He could stay aboard, hoping that when the dead man was identified, it would lead to the truth of that attack; and if that were established, his story about the others would be believed more readily.

Would it?

He could have killed Gann and Maisie; he had had the opportunity, as the ship's officers would find out. He would probably find himself locked as tightly as in a vice.

At least the vacillation had done one thing; forced him to look at every angle. He had no reasonable chance aboard. So, whatever the risks, he had to try to get ashore; at least he would have some kind of chance in New York. Newspapers would tell him a lot, and he would be able to find Olive Johns.

He had her address, hadn't he?

He could find out where Pirran went to in New York, too. Don't forget Pirran might have the key to the mystery from start to finish. Not 'why was he dead?' but why was he alive?

Was there a chance to get off the ship?

Whittaker got up, and looked at himself in the mirror. His blue eyes lacked their sparkle and their colour. Good. He had plenty of experience, and could mix with a crowd easily enough, but would have to overcome passport and customs difficulties, which were formidable in New York.

Unsurpassable?

Then, he heard a sound at the door. It wasn't loud, but it seemed to detonate something inside him. He swung round sharply—and saw the door handle moving. Then the door opened. So someone else had a pass-key.

He moved swiftly to one side, but wasn't quick enough. The door opened wider, and a man stood there.

He had no knife and no gun, and presented no obvious danger, but he wore a uniform.

Whittaker recognised him at once: the Master-at-Arms, the man responsible, under the Captain, for security and safety on board the great *Queen B*. He had the look of a St. Bernard, kindly, shaggy, yet carried menace. The difficult thing was to look genuinely surprised, even a little annoyed, but to do nothing which might heighten suspicion. Yet a fact remained: they were after him already. Any chance seemed slimmer and more dangerous now.

The man didn't look abashed at his uninvited entry.

'Evening, sir,' he said bluffly. 'Just making sure you're in. Captain Morrison would like a word with you; he'll be here in a minute.'

Whittaker said, 'Who?' just to gain time. He didn't think he had let himself down, yet. The Master-at-Arms repeated, 'Captain Morrison, sir,' and then gave a broad grin. 'Mind if I come in?'

Whittaker waved a hand.

'I don't see how I can do anything about it, and since you're here you might as well be comfortable. I hope it won't be too long. I was just going to turn in.'

'Shouldn't be many minutes, sir.'

'That's something.' Whittaker waited until the Master-at-Arms had closed the door, and then said, 'Care for a drink?'

'Not now, sir, thanks.'

'Mind if I do?' asked Whittaker, 'or I'll start nodding before the Captain gets here.' He poured out a whisky-and-soda, not too strong, and sipped. 'What have I done to deserve the Captain's personal attention?'

'He'll tell you, sir.'

'Hm,' said Whittaker, as if he were fighting down his annoyance; 'I suppose he will. Anything to do with the trouble on the staircase?'

The Master-at-Arms didn't answer, but turned to the door instead. A man was approaching with quick, firm footsteps; the approach of a man who knew just what he was about.

The Master-at-Arms opened the door, and the stocky Captain of the *Queen B*. stepped into the cabin. Morrison had the weathered appearance to be expected of a sailor, and that other curious quality of looking as if he was always awake; that he never slept. His eyes were honey-brown and bright; the crows-feet at the corners looked as if they had been there from birth. At five feet eight he was shorter even than Whittaker, yet his breadth of shoulder and thickness of chest stopped him from looking small. He had full lips and a broad, broken nose. It was in his power to send Whittaker below, to keep him prisoner until they got back to Southampton and the police could take over. He was the absolute authority here—and he felt that there were good reasons for coming in person to see Whittaker.

'Ah, Mr. Whittaker,' he greeted. 'I don't think we've met.' He made no attempt to shake hands. 'As I believe you know, there's been a most unfortunate occurrence here tonight.'

Was he too bluff?—too hearty?

Whittaker said dryly, 'Yes, I gathered so.'

'Did you see anything of the occurrence?' That was blunt and to the point, touched with formality, and it was easy to answer convincingly.

'No,' Whittaker said flatly.

'Have you ever seen the dead man?'

That held a plain enough implication—a man had been found, and obviously it was the man on the stairs. Not Gann —yet. Not the blonde. They had got on to him because of the 'occurrence' which he had thought least likely to point his way.

'Not to my knowledge,' he said.

'I'd like you to see him,' Morrison said. 'Have you any objection?' He wasn't going to waste time; he was going to use all his authority, and it looked as if he were very sure of himself. This might be a time to react badly.

'None at all,' Whittaker said coldly, 'but I don't see why it's necessary to come to see me at this hour. If I can help, I will, but I hope it won't take long. Where is he?'

'Just outside,' Morrison said, and didn't even begin an apology.

In fact, the dead man was on a stretcher which rested on a trolley in the passage. Sailors were at either end of the stretcher, two sergeants-at-arms near them. In its way, this was quite a show of strength. The dead man's face was uncovered, and there was no sign of injury; no blemish.

Morrison and the Master-at-Arms watched Whittaker intently, as if they meant to take a mental photograph of his expression, and make sure that they couldn't forget it.

'Know him?' asked Morrison.

'I've seen him about on board,' Whittaker answered, 'but I've never spoken to him. Who is he?' That was the simple truth. He was still curt, and acting as if he were annoyed.

'Just a passenger,' said Morrison. 'Until tonight we'd no reason to suspect him of any form of crime or subterfuge. However, tonight he was seen to go into a cabin where two men were.' Morrison paused, as if to let that sink in, but almost certainly to add to Whittaker's uncertainty. Whittaker couldn't escape the obvious question: why had they come straight here? It wasn't chance. Out of a thousand people they chose to question him.

Morrison went on, in the same smooth voice, while looking down at the dead man:

'He is suspected of killing one of those two men and robbing the other. Certain articles found in his pocket prove to have come from Mr. Pirran's. . . .'

Whittaker had just enough warning to know what to do; how to change his attitude. In one way there was cause for relief, for now he knew why they had come to him so quickly.

He burst out, 'Pirran's cabin?' He moved swiftly, and grabbed Morrison's arm. For the moment he must have looked so menacing that the Master-at-Arms moved to intercept him, and he told himself that no one could even suspect that he knew about Bob's death. And he kept his head. He flashed words out which should fool them completely. 'Pirran? Is he dead? *Is he?*'

Morrison was still watching intently, but Whittaker felt an easing of the tension. He had admitted reason to think that Pirran was dead, had shown not the slightest indication that he knew about Bob.

If they had come to find out whether he knew about that, then he had fooled them.

Morrison moved back a little, before he said in a quieter voice, 'No, Mr. Pirran isn't dead.'

Whittaker began to speak, and then stopped. Behaving like this was almost an offence to the dead, but he had no choice because he was in such desperate need of time and a chance to get off this ship. In a hard, abrupt voice he said:

'Not Gann?'

'I'm afraid so, Mr. Whittaker,' Morrison said, and looked as if he hated bringing the news.

Whittaker simply stood there, tense-faced, bleak-eyed. He didn't move, and he made the silence uncomfortable. Then:

'Where is he?' he demanded.

'Mr. Gann is still in Pirran's room,' Morrison said. 'There is a lot of evidence that the other dead man went in, killed Gann, and searched the room. He had a pass-key, and would have no trouble getting in.' Morrison paused, then asked quietly, 'Were you a close personal friend of Gann?'

Whittaker could answer this in a way that might lead to trouble; in fact, he had been so intent on making them think that he had no idea that Bob was dead, that he had over-played his hand. Would a man show such a reaction to the news of the death of a man he had known only for a few days?

He had to make the best of it.

'Yes,' he said. 'Not an old friend, but——'

'You were working together, weren't you?'

Morrison must have known that they were.

'I'd been given instructions to leave the two rooms at your disposal,' Morrison went on, 'because Gann had some kind of official position in Washington. What were you doing on board?' Now, Morrison's manner was completely relaxed, and Whittaker began to believe that he had escaped any urgent danger, and had won himself time.

Whittaker hesitated, and let them see that he didn't like the question. That wouldn't matter; if he began to talk as if what he said didn't matter, they might take it as a sign of nerves. He had to decide not only what to tell them, but also how.

Slowly, and with a kind of reluctant deliberation, he told part of the truth. As he did so, he tried to see how the minds of these two men would work, now that he had established 'close friendship' with Gann. He believed that he had won their respect, and that whatever suspicion they'd had was gone for the time being. But he had probably been seen near the staircase, and they might know more than they'd let him think, and they hadn't yet explained just why they had come here. Even if he had fooled them for the time being, he mustn't fool himself. At best, he had gained a few hours' respite, but even that wasn't certain, and they might hold him; confine him to his cabin, if no worse.

When Maisie's body was found and the steward questioned, there would be no option; he would be held. Whatever he did must be between now and the time they found the blonde, and he might not have long.

They might even have searched his cabin already; might be playing cat-and-mouse.

He fought down that fear, but was almost at screaming pitch when Morrison said quietly: 'I see. And there's been no cause for alarm about Pirran until tonight?'

'No. Not even tonight.'

It was all right; he had fooled them.

'Has this man,' Morrison pointed to the body on the stretcher, 'been near Pirran?'

'Not to my knowledge.'

'Did Pirran tell you why he was in this danger?'

'No,' But one of these days he would—if he, Whittaker, could get at him now, he'd talk all right.

'H'm,' grunted Morrison. 'Well, we'll have to tackle Pirran as soon as we can.' His attitude had changed completely, and the way he said that almost brought Whittaker within the scope of the ship's personnel. The simplicity of Whittaker's answers had probably helped to make Morrison better disposed. Keep him that way, but remember one thing was certain: it wouldn't be long before he got round to Maisie the blonde, and he would soon want to question her. When he searched, his mood would change in a flash.

Whittaker said abruptly:

'Mind if I see Gann?'

'No, of course not,' Morrison said.

So they weren't going to keep him in his cabin.

In fact, as they left together, he sensed a softening in Morrison's attitude; as if the Captain were dealing with a man who was suffering an acute personal loss. The Master-at-Arms was more like a St. Bernard than ever, as if he were eager to come to Whittaker's rescue. It wasn't difficult to keep up the impression—and it wasn't pretence of any kind.

Gann *had* mattered to him.

A man you had known for a few days could be as real a friend as one whom you had known for years.

There was a lot about Gann which Whittaker didn't know. His friends, his habits, his recreations, his hobbies. And there was a lot about Gann's family that he didn't know, either; but as Whittaker stood in the cabin which had been turned into a morgue, and looked down at the dead man, he felt as if he had known not only Gann but his family for a long time.

A picture of Gann's wife kept coming into his mind's eye. It had done, from the time he had first seen it; it wasn't one of those things that could be put into words, but here was a woman whom he could get to know quickly; who, in an odd way, he *did* know. He could tell the rest of the world about it, and the rest of the world would laugh, but he knew that he was talking sense to himself.

He would have to see her, soon.

As it was, he stood on one side of the bench where Bob Gann lay. His face wasn't touched; it was easy to think that he was not dead, but asleep. There was a hint of vitality, even in death.

Morrison was watching Whittaker closely.

At last, he said, 'We'd better go.'

The Master-at-Arms put a hand on Whittaker's shoulder, and kept it there as they turned towards the door. At first it didn't mean a thing; Whittaker was just seeing those faces in his mind's eye, and wishing with a kind of desperate folly that the dead man could come alive again. Then, as they reached the passage, the grip on his shoulder seemed to become tighter; as if it were not going to be slackened, and was in fact the grip of arrest.

Whittaker fought back the impulse to shake himself free.

'Mr. Whittaker,' Morrison said, 'you've told me that you were employed by Pirran to guard him because of attacks on his life, and that Mr. Gann was doing the same thing. I know that you had made arrangements with the owners, and I want you to understand that I'm not complaining

41

about anything you've done up to now. But there is one thing I want to say to you.'

Whittaker didn't speak, just waited; and the pressure at his shoulder grew tighter—there was no longer any doubt the Master-at-Arms was gripping him with a purpose.

He waited, looking into the Captain's eyes.

CHAPTER V

WARNING

'FROM now on, you can forget your job,' Morrison said at last. 'From now on, I will watch Mr. Pirran and anyone else who may need watching. I may need to question you again, but whether I do or don't, I want one thing to be clearly understood. You are to keep away from Pirran's cabin. Don't start investigating on your own account.'

Here was welcome relief again, almost assurance that Morrison was not yet suspicious. He was a private eye, doing his job, and being warned not to carry on with it while he remained on board. Obviously they were going to leave him to his own resources. That was fine.

'May I have your assurance that you'll leave well alone?' Morrison asked, sharply.

Whittaker didn't speak, but took his cigarette-case out of his pocket. Morrison shook his head when it was proffered, and Whittaker lit a cigarette. They had started to walk on again, and turned into an empty cabin at a word from the Captain. In the past few seconds, Morrison's manner and that of the Master-at-Arms had hardened, but it didn't matter; in some ways it was a good thing.

Everything Whittaker did had to be directed towards one object: getting ashore.

'I don't want there to be the slightest misunderstanding,' Morrison said. 'I want your full assurance that you won't attempt to see Pirran or make any inquiry on your own account. If you don't give it, Mr. Whittaker, I shall have to make sure that you can't do either thing.'

Whittaker let himself smile, tautly.

'So it's an order.'

'It's an order.'

Whittaker drew deeply on his cigarette.

'I don't know how much you know about my job, Captain Morrison,' he said, 'but you know plenty about yours; you're in charge of this ship, and whatever the risk to yourself, you always try to make sure that every passenger and every member of the crew is safe. Isn't that so?'

Morrison's eyes were narrowed and steely.

'Supposing it is?'

'I just want to show you what you are asking,' Whittaker said. 'I am a private inquiry agent. Most of my jobs are humdrum, but every now and again a big one crops up. This is a big one. Pirran is paying me a lot of money. If I let him down I let myself down, and in some ways that is more important. I have to be sure that no one is taking the slightest risk with Pirran.'

'No one will be.'

Whittaker drew on the cigarette again.

'That's easy to say. But I would like to know what kind of precautions you propose to take, Captain Morrison. You may not think so, but I'm an expert at my job. You might overlook something that's important.'

Morrison smiled faintly, and the Master-at-Arms had a more shaggy and amiable look than ever.

'I don't think you need worry,' Morrison said. 'Mr. Corbin here was with the Surrey County Police for twenty-five years and you might call him an expert, too. You needn't worry about Pirran.'

'How are you going to protect him?'

'I don't feel called——' Morrison began.

'Don't misunderstand me,' Whittaker said, reasoningly. 'I can't make you tell me any more than I can stop you from putting me in irons, but unless I'm satisfied that Pirran is safe, I'm not making any promise to you or to anyone else. That way, my conscience will be clear. The other way——' he shrugged. The cigarette was already burned halfway down, and he could feel the warmth against his lips; but he didn't look away from the Captain's eyes.

Morrison glanced sharply at the Master-at-Arms. Then:

'Mr. Pirran will be confined to his cabin until we reach New York,' he said. 'No one will be able to see him without full authorisation—and that includes you. Does your job finish at New York?'

'Yes, it does.'

'Then you haven't to be patient for long.'

'All right.' Whittaker became brisker. 'I won't try to see him, you have my word on it. But you may be making a mistake, after all.' He grinned at the ex-policeman, Corbin. 'At least, I warned you.'

Corbin smiled back.

'Pirran may know a lot more than he's told me,' Whittaker said. 'After Gann's death, he'll probably be more frightened even than he is now. If anything has been stolen from him, it might loosen his tongue, but—how do we know that he's not playing some game outside the law?'

'We don't know.'

'That's the right answer,' Whittaker agreed. 'We don't know. If he's a criminal, he certainly won't talk to you. He isn't likely to talk to the police, either—but he might talk to me. For one thing, he knows that I'm in his employ. For another, he'll probably think that anything he told me would be in confidence.'

Whittaker paused.

'Wouldn't it be?' asked Morrison, dryly.

'I'm under no obligation to Pirran or anyone else to keep material facts from the authorities,' answered Whittaker smoothly. 'I've reason to believe that Pirran keeps within the law, that's one thing; if I've reason to believe that he looks like stepping outside it, that's another. In any case, if I were to withhold information which might lead to the arrest of a murderer, I would never be able to keep my office open in London—Scotland Yard would make sure of that. The issue couldn't be simpler. Pirran might talk to me, but almost certainly won't talk to you. Why not let me have a go at him?'

The Master-at-Arms was smiling faintly.

'At the moment he's asleep,' said the Captain. 'It's a drugged sleep, too. The ship's doctor doesn't expect him to come round until the morning. That gives us time to think over your suggestion, Mr. Whittaker.'

'I think it's a good suggestion,' Whittaker said.

'I wouldn't mind knowing your real reason for making it,' put in the Master-at-Arms unexpectedly. He looked massive, and amiable, but it was obvious that he could be dangerous and the danger might be close. 'You wouldn't be more interested in catching Gann's killer than finding out more from Pirran, Mr. Whittaker, would you?'

He was no fool.

Whittaker said quietly, 'That job ought to interest you, too, Mr. Corbin.'

He wasn't surprised when both men chuckled.

'You go and get some rest,' Morrison said. 'We shouldn't need to disturb you again, Mr. Whittaker.'

Whittaker said, 'Thanks,' but didn't turn towards the door at once. He made it clear that there was something else on his mind, and they waited for him to speak. He took his time. He lit another cigarette, and as he did so, told himself that he would be safe until morning unless the breaks went the wrong way. It wasn't likely that they would find the blonde Maisie until the morning.

They would probably wait before questioning any other passengers, but they would talk to the crew. They would find out from the bar steward that Pirran had been with the blonde and the brunette, and then they would start asking questions among the stewards—and they would learn that he had come out of Maisie's room.

He had to decide just how far to go.

If *he* told these two about Maisie and the other girl and Pirran, they would have reason to believe that he was being wholly frank, and above everything else wanted to help. Get it straight. If he told them about the blonde and they did go and find her dead, surely it would be in his favour; they wouldn't expect him to tell them about a girl who was dead in her cabin and whose death might lead to him.

'What is it?' Morrison asked.

Whittaker said: 'You'll probably say that it's none of my business, but Pirran got drunk tonight. If he's drugged and right out, then the drug could have been put in his drink.' He gave a quick grin at the ex-policeman. 'I know I'm teaching my grandmother, but there's one thing I can tell you that you may not know yet. Time saved is sometimes a help in investigation.'

'Try to save us some,' urged the Master-at-Arms.

'There were two girls with Pirran in the bar,' Whittaker said. 'They helped him to his cabin. A blonde, whose name was Maisie, I think, and a brunette whose name I didn't catch. I was very interested in them, thinking they were probably after Pirran for any money they could get. But there was a chance that they were the people I was looking for. Gann and I agreed about that. He was on duty, and watched them as well as for Pirran.'

The Master-at-Arms said warmly: 'That could be very useful. Thanks.'

'I didn't want to leave anything undone, either,' Whittaker said.

He turned towards the door.

He had got away with it so far; but he might have put a rope round his own neck. He kept outwardly cool while he was with them; but as soon as he left them and walked towards his own cabin, he felt choked. He didn't hurry. He actually went up on deck for a few minutes, looking at the dark mystery of the swirling sea, where it shone like black oil in the lights of the ship. There were more lights on land, too, as they drew nearer to New York itself.

He went back to his cabin.

He knew, within a second of stepping inside, that it had been searched; the Master-at-Arms had almost certainly arranged that to take place while he was being questioned. A wide-awake man would have discovered that a girl had been in that bed recently, but he couldn't guess much else. The things which had been disturbed had been put back almost in the same place, but one which had been moved was the photograph of Bob Gann's wife.

It was too near the edge, now.

Whittaker touched it, to push it to a safer place, then felt impelled to pick it up and study the dark hair, the fine eyes, the clear-cut features. She was smiling faintly, as if at someone who mattered to her. There was a touch of intimacy which couldn't be mistaken.

He put it down, slowly.

Yes, he wanted Gann's killer. First and last.

Unless they went to look for the blonde at once, he had given himself a chance to find him.

In half an hour, he was in bed, and no one disturbed him.

He had opened the door of the cabin once, and seen a sergeant-at-arms in sight; that might mean they were watching him, might simply mean that they were being very careful. He kept thinking of everything—Gann, his wife, the dead blonde, the man whose neck he had broken . . .

All that faded.

How could he get away?

How could any passenger get ashore?

Could he swim for it? The coast of Long Island wasn't so far away.

He rejected the notion as soon as it came; he was a fair swimmer, but that attempt would be crazy.

How could he get off the ship?

Suddenly, he saw a possibility, and it made him grin in the darkness. He listened intently, and heard footsteps. He got up and went to the door, opened it a crack, and looked into the lighted passage. There was the sergeant-at-arms, talking to a steward. The sergeant-at-arms was in navy-blue uniform, and was a man of average size and build; Whittaker's size. He was likely to be there for a long time, certainly until dawn; and when he left, he would almost certainly be replaced by another man.

Unless Maisie's body were found there would be no drastic action until the *Queen B.* berthed. So, he had a little time. If he judged the right moment and played his cards well, he could leave the *Queen B.* as a uniformed sergeant-at-arms, carrying all the proper authority and as safe from suspicion as anyone was likely to be.

He needed a little rest first, but could wake when he wanted to start out.

He needed some luck, too.

CHAPTER VI

CUSTOMS CUTTER

WHITTAKER looked out of the porthole towards the calm sea and the fabulous skyline. He couldn't see enough of it. In earlier years he had seen it passing gently by a dozen times, and could feast his eyes as often as he got the chance. More than once, having settled in his New York hotel, he had taken the ferry to Staten Island, so that he could watch

47

the skyline going to the island and coming back. He could look at the Statute of Liberty without feeling stirred, but that skyline . . .

The sun shone on the tall buildings.

He knew that the ship was moving slowly, and that police as well as the pilot and customs were on board. He could imagine what the scene was like, on the main decks, the indignation and disappointment of passengers, the shocked comments when the truth began to spread.

Had Maisie been found?

Whittaker didn't know yet, and didn't want to know. His chance was here, now, and he wouldn't have another. At the awful worst, he would hang for a murder he had not committed. At best, he would be taken back to England and probably stand trial; and he would have no chance to find Pirran; to find a murderer; to avenge Gann.

If he could get ashore . . .

If he tried and failed, he might damn himself—but no more than Maisie's body and the steward's evidence would.

He was in his pyjamas when he opened the door. The sergeant-at-arms looked round promptly.

Whittaker stifled a yawn, then managed to grin.

'Spare me a moment, will you?'

The sergeant-at-arms came at once; no kind of danger appeared to threaten. Whittaker yawned again and stood aside. The other man hesitated on the threshold, as if reluctant to go in.

'What——' he began.

Whittaker gripped his wrist, twisted, and brought him into the cabin. No one else was in sight. He sent the man spinning across to the bed, closed the door swiftly, and went after his victim like a bullet.

Two sharp blows, and the sergeant-at-arms collapsed.

*　　　*　　　*

The man's clothes fitted Whittaker.

He had a special customs and dock pass.

*　　　*　　　*

The pass took Whittaker through the customs shed, which had a forlorn and deserted look, in spite of the dozens, probably hundreds, of uniformed examiners who stood

48

about waiting for the passengers. By now, this shed should be a seething mass of activity; as it was, no luggage at all had been brought ashore. The officers stood about in little groups, talking, smoking. Porters, most of them coloured men, looked disconsolate. Whittaker took his pass to one of the officers, had it countersigned, and then went to the lift which took him down to street level. No one showed the slightest suspicion of him.

It was half-past eight, and already warm.

A long line of taxis waited, and at sight of him, a dozen drivers braced themselves, as if they believed that the long wait was over at last. The first was broad and bow-legged, hatless, and wearing a linen coat.

'Cab, sir?'

'Thanks. Hotel Commodore, please.'

'Sure,' the cabby said.

It didn't take long. There, behind Whittaker, was the mass of shipping in the Cunard docks, and, some distance off-shore, the *Queen B.* She would soon be alongside. The sun blazed on the Hudson River, on masts, on funnels, on tugs, on the glass in the buildings in New Jersey, on a million television aerials. An aeroplane droned. Traffic was thin for the first few hundred yards, until they turned into 42nd Street; immediately, it began to thicken. Cabs, cars, trucks seemed to be trying to pass one another at the same time. Everyone seemed in a hurry, every driver looked as if he hadn't a care in the world. That was a nonchalance that Whittaker enjoyed; and a freedom he could hardly believe in. But he had it, and he also had his one great asset: the ability to get lost in a crowd. He never stood out as an individual unless he wanted to.

Above him were those tall buildings.

Whittaker was never tired of gaping; never failed to be surprised that the really tall ones were few and far between, dominant overlords. Even now. Held up at cross-roads, he saw the square, pale might of the RKO building and Rockefeller Centre. Then, lights changed, the line of traffic leapt; he seemed to be swung right and left and left and right before they pulled up at the hotel. It looked huge; it didn't give an inkling of what there was inside.

He went into the hotel, casually acknowledged by a porter who looked Irish, up the steps, and into the enormous central hall. It looked like an orange grove; what must surely be real orange-trees, standing in huge yellow tubs, were dotted about; the fruit looked too real to be tied on. He found himself smiling; nothing had changed although everything had changed. He didn't linger, but walked briskly towards the entrance to Grand Central Station. He walked along the concourse, past the shops and news stands, past a dozen snack-bars where men and women were having breakfast. He reached the station itself, stepped into the mammoth main hall, and looked up at the giant advertisements, unbelieving, as he always was when here.

In the centre was the Information Bureau.

He walked towards this, and was dwarfed. Every footstep sounded impudent, every human being looked insignificant—and there were masses of them, coming out of the doors which led to the platforms, which were hidden away behind dark doors.

'Help you?' a youth asked at the desk.

'Can you give me the times of trains to Scarsdale?' Whittaker spoke casually, in an accent that would pass for American or Canadian; wasn't at all 'English'.

'Sure. Lower level, every half-hour on the hour and half-hour. You can't miss it,'

'Fine,' said Whittaker. He moved away briskly towards a sign which directed him towards the lower level. He didn't go down, though, but along the concourse again and up to street level. He had been in the man-made caverns of the station for twenty minutes, but it seemed much hotter when he appeared above ground again. Everyone seemed in a hurry, and there was more hooting traffic and more jostling pedestrians; the restaurants were crowded. Shops were open or opening. He went briskly to Broadway, and turned right; and a few blocks along, reached a shop with a huge window, and the slogan: GOOD CLOTHES FOR MEN. It was open. He didn't feel that anyone was on his heels yet, but they might start sooner than he expected, and he hadn't a lot of time.

A middle-aged man came up.

'Help you, sir?'

'Do you have a linen coat?' asked Whittaker, in the newly-acquired voice. 'One that will fit me?'

'There isn't a man in New York we can't fit,' the man

50

assured him. 'This way, sir, please.'

In two minutes Whittaker was looking at his reflection in a biscuit-coloured linen coat which was far too big round the waist and too long in the sleeves.

'You want to try our medium size?' The clerk's eyes were doing all the smiling.

Whittaker was easily satisfied; as satisfied, too, that this man didn't dream he was talking to an Englishman; that was important—vital.

Whittaker went out, carrying a box branded GOOD CLOTHES FOR MEN, and returned to Grand Central. The concourse and the great hall were swarming with people, and everyone looked hot. He had some coffee and bacon and eggs, sitting at a bar. Then he went to the nearest public lockers; those empty had a key in the lock as usual; for fifty cents he could get the key out, and use a locker. He chose a locker, put his parcel and other oddments inside, slipped the key into his pocket, then went down to the Scarsdale booking office and on to the platform. Streams of people were coming off the arrival trains; the platform he went on was empty, only a dozen or so passengers were sitting in the train itself. He settled down, with the *New York Herald Tribune* and the *Mirror*, and waited; on the dot of ten o'clock the train drew out of the station.

For a while it seemed as if it were going through a tunnel which had no end, but after ten minutes or so, daylight came.

Soon New York lay behind him.

He skimmed through the newspapers, but didn't think much about what he read. He kept seeing Bob Gann. He was going to see Bob Gann's image for a long time.

And the man who had killed Gann had been lying in wait for him.

Why?

The train stopped, the guard called out, amiably, and made a special journey to tell Whittaker the next stop was Scarsdale. The guard would remember him, but only vaguely.

'Thanks a lot,' Whittaker said, and stood up.

'You're welcome,' the guard said.

You're welcome. . . .

Several taxis, more subdued in colour than in the city,

were waiting outside the station. The suburb looked small, pleasant, tree-filled and hot; everyone looked hot, and Whittaker had seldom felt hotter. He went to the first taxi; it wasn't here that he needed to cover his traces, but after he'd got back to New York. The one thing he took for granted was that he would not run into any trouble until he had seen Mrs. Gann, and told her the ugly truth.

Two things drove him forward.

He had an odd quirk of feeling that he owed it to Gann that he couldn't let anyone else break the news coldly or brutally or even kindly but without understanding. That would have been enough in itself, but there was another thing, no more than a possibility: that Mrs. Gann might have some idea why Gann had been killed.

Crazy?

The hundredth chance was the only one that mattered every time it came off.

'Grantley Avenue, sir,' said the middle-aged cabby. He wore a linen suit, the same colour as Whittaker's coat except where honest toil had darkened it, and a peaked cap. 'You know the house?'

'Number Forty-five.'

'Oh, sure,' said the cabby. 'Bob Gann's place.'

'That's right.'

'Have you there in ten minutes,' the cabby promised, and started off as if he had all day to spare; but the breeze coming in at the windows had a semblance of coolness. They drove past tall, dark blocks of apartment buildings, then over a bridge, then off the main road. Suddenly, they were lost in trees and in coolness. The trees grew tall and stately, the small leaves had an almost transparent greenness, and they not only cooled the air, they softened the outlines of the houses on either side. The road twisted and turned, until a signpost, pointing up a steep hill, read: GRANTLEY AVENUE.

'There it is, that fourth house on your right,' said the cabby. 'See that girl playing with the doll? That's Mimi Gann. Sure is a sweet kid.'

Whittaker felt his jaws tighten.

'Young Bob's at school,' the cabby said. 'Spitting image of his father, young Bob.'

Whittaker didn't speak.

'Well, here you are,' the cabby said.

The girl, who was as fair as Gann had been dark, looked up from the pram and two dolls with a wide-eyed curiosity. Her eyes were blue. She just wanted to know who the stranger was, why he had come here. She didn't move but watched him. He had to force a smile, because he was realising exactly what he had come into; the kind of disaster he was bringing here. His feet dragged.

He reached the front door: it stood open. He heard the whirr of a vacuum cleaner. Somehow, the normality of that, and the bright eyes of the child, made him feel far worse. He raised a hand to press the bell, when he was aware of the child behind him, at the nearest grassy spot.

'Just go right in,' she said, 'I'll tell my mummy.'

He swung round. 'Will you? That's fine!' His smile was a little easier as he watched her turn and rush towards the back of the house. He wondered why she didn't go straight through the front doorway; but it didn't matter.

He stepped over the threshold of what looked like a well-furnished home. He heard the whine of the taxi as it went up the steep road leading from here. He took another step forward, and a man behind the door said:

'Stop where you are, and don't move.'

CHAPTER VII

BOB GANN'S WIFE

THE man's voice was low-pitched and hard with the kind of hardness which meant business. Whittaker stopped quite still. His hands were empty and by his sides; he left them there, where the man behind him could see them. If the man were armed, and if he raised his hand . . .

Stillness froze him.

The vacuum cleaner whirred, and above the sound there came the child's voice, shrilly.

'Mummy, there's a man!'

There were other sounds, perhaps other voices, but the vacuum cleaner didn't stop. Then a door closed, and the sound was cut off, although it lingered in the distance. All that had taken a few seconds, and they were seconds while icy water seemed to trickle down Whittaker's spine. He kept looking about him. This was a long, narrow hall. Two arched doorways, without doors, led off this, one into a big sunlit room, another into a passage. On one side of the passage was a staircase, painted white, with a half landing.

Near Whittaker, and close to the passage, was a mirror. In the room beyond as well as in this hall, there were a grand piano, pictures, comfortable chairs, expensive ornaments and a thick carpet.

If he moved his head a little he might be able to see his own reflection in the mirror and that of the man behind him.

One shot would be plenty.

The man said, 'Stay right where you are; let me get a look at you.' He moved slowly. The vacuum cleaner still hummed.

Whittaker saw that he had a gun with a silencer: and was looking down at a photograph he held in his hand.

His? Whittaker's?

'Okay,' the man said. 'You're the guy Pirran saw in London, you've come to the right place.' There was the lash of menace in his words. 'What did Pirran tell you?'

Whittaker didn't try to speak.

He heard the hissing intake of breath, and knew fear greater than he had ever known it. He heard the click; the kind of sound that a trigger might make being squeezed. He kept absolutely still, and his teeth seemed to grind into one another. Then the shot came. The subdued zutt of sound was vicious. He felt the wind past his face, saw the wood of the staircase splinter as the bullet bit deep.

'Don't hold out on me, Whittaker,' the man said. 'We haven't much time. What did Pirran tell you?'

Whittaker said heavily, 'He wanted a bodyguard; he was nervous.'

'That's right, he was nervous,' the gunman said. 'Did he tell you why?'

'He'd been attacked——'

The man said roughly: 'Stop stalling! Did Pirran tell you why he was on the spot?'

The truthful answer was 'No.'

'No,' Whittaker said.

'Did he tell Gann?'

'If so, Gann didn't tell me.'

'Whittaker, I've warned you plenty,' said the man with the gun. 'Maybe you don't have to answer. Okay—you don't have to live. See that hole in the wall? Imagine what it would look like in your head!'

Whittaker said: 'Pirran wanted a private eye. That's me. He asked the Embassy in London for protection. They gave Gann the job. No one told me anything more than I've told you.'

'If you're lying——'

'I don't lie when a gun's at my back,' Whittaker said heavily.

'So you don't?' The other man seemed almost to be stalling; he paused, and then said abruptly, 'You see that packet Pirran had?'

It was easy to sound surprised.

'Packet? What pack——?' Whittaker stopped.

He could see the other's face in the mirror, and didn't like what he saw. A preview of death. He'd been near it on the *Queen B*, but not so desperately close.

He said: 'Okay! Shoot to kill friend. But why pick on me? Give me the reason, before you squeeze the trigger.' He spoke to try to gain time—time even to think in, to seek some way of winning even a chance of life.

The man said, 'You've seen too much, and maybe Pirran talked, so . . .'

That would be an answer. Whoever wanted Pirran dead knew that Pirran had hired help, believed Pirran might have talked of some vital thing. He hadn't to Whittaker; but he could so easily have done.

So Gann had died.

He was to die.

Whittaker said in a choky voice, 'Give me two minutes, give me——'

He broke off, and leapt desperately to one side. As he moved, he dug into his pocket for his gun, but knew that he hadn't a real chance.

The distance between them was six feet; there were several bullets left in the other's gun, and there was a killer-look in his eyes. Whittaker hadn't time even to touch his weapon, hardly time to pray; just to know that death was coming to him as it had come to Gann. A split second of understanding and of fear, and . . .

A window in the big room crashed in.

The noise was shattering, startling him out of the grip of his own terror. It made the man with the gun swing round. Through the arched doorway they saw the smashed window, billowing curtain, the glass which looked like a huge star, and a woman standing on the other side of the window. She had a mop in her hand, the mop with which she had smashed the window. She stood as if transfixed, although in the distance a vacuum cleaner whined.

The gunman's hand raised, the gun covered the woman in a split second.

'Friend,' said Whittaker.

He made the word crackle, and he made the gunman turn. He had his own gun out, now, and fired and struck the man's wrist. It happened as quickly as that. Roar—flash—whine—and gasp. Shot for shot, a tug at his shoulder, and a splotch of red on the other man's wrist. The gun with the silencer dropped, clattering.

For a moment, it was like a tableau.

Then the door which had been closed, opened, and Mimi Gann came running in. Only the crack of the shot would have brought her. She came hurrying in, and must have seen the shattered wrist and the blood, because she stopped close to Whittaker, with her hands raised, and her blue eyes so wide open and rounded that they just weren't true.

Then:

'Mimi!' screamed the woman at the window. 'Mimi!'

The man who held up Whittaker was moving, now, racing towards the passage. Whittaker could shoot and bring him down, and risk hurting the child.

'Mimi!' cried the woman.

The man rushed along the passage. Whittaker tried to get past the child, but in her terror she dodged the way he moved, and he almost fell in trying to avoid her. He put his hands down, to grasp and to set her on one side, but as he did so she began to scream, as if the terror had only now come to the surface. And she kicked as she screamed.

56

'Oh, Mimi, Mimi!' The woman's voice was further away, and she came running; Whittaker could hear her footsteps, and the footsteps of the man. The screaming child was a barrier more solid than any wall or door; he couldn't leave the child until the woman had arrived.

The woman came from the passage.

She didn't speak, but the burning dread in her eyes cooled when she saw that the child was not hurt. She swooped forward and downwards, with a kind of graceful pride and lifted Mimi, first high and then very close. She didn't look at Whittaker, only at the child.

Whittaker thrust his way past her. The passage led to the kitchen and the back door. From there, he saw the drive of the house next door, and a gleaming blue car, which began to move into the road. He couldn't see who was at the wheel, but he could guess. The engine was purring. There were trees between him and the car, and if he fired there was no way of being sure that he would stop the car or hit the driver. He couldn't see the number. The car gathered speed and spurted up the steep road. So Whittaker stood and waited until it went out of sight, and the sky-blue colour faded from among the trees.

Now, all was quiet.

A hint of a breeze murmured among the delicate leaves of the beech and birch trees. A long way off, a car engine sounded. That was all. The next-door house was fifty yards or more away, and the windows seemed closed; and he could not see any other house nearby. This was a little clearing in a wood, with houses dotted about it, quietness which the shots inside Number Forty-five had obviously not seriously disturbed.

No one came.

Inside, the child was sobbing.

Whittaker went in, through the spotless kitchen, a kitchen which any woman would envy, which was still almost a dream to most English housewives. Chromium gleamed, tiles sparkled, a refrigerator nearly as tall as the door purred with a smug, machine-made satisfaction. The child's crying was muffled, as if she were pressed tightly against her mother. It was as if she had some premonition of the blow which was coming to them both.

Whittaker slowed down as he reached the living-room.

57

All thought of the man who had escaped, and all thought of the fact that a man had been waiting for him, here, went out of his mind.

There was mother and child.

Mrs. Gann was standing by the side of a huge armchair. The child stood on it, tight against her mother, whose arms encompassed her, as if only they could offer true protection. The muffled sobbing kept on and on, with Mimi's head buried in her mother's breast, for her comfort, her solace, her desperately needed reassurance.

The sobbing seemed to quieten.

Sensing that she was being watched, the woman turned her head.

She was tall. She had a queenliness which nothing could take away—a kind of magnificence. Her face had pallor and her eyes a false brightness, but she had the striking looks which her photograph had shown, and of which Gann had seemed so proud. Her hair, braided and worn like a crown of spun gold, was like ripe corn, and her eyes were grey like the light of a clear dawn. It didn't matter that she had stood outside the window, face set in horror, or that she had come running and screaming because of her fear. She stood there, like the mother of all creation, pressing her child against her with desperation which told of longing. It told of other things, too: and as she looked at Whittaker, her eyes betrayed fear.

The child was much quieter.

Whittaker stood waiting, huge and still and silent. He had to tell this woman that her man was dead. He wished he were a million miles away, but he stood here with the task close by him, and one he knew that he could not shirk. Nor could he speak, until the child had gone and he was alone with her mother.

'He's gone,' he said, and meant the gunman. Gann's wife realised that, although the words had the bitterness of irony for him. 'May I have a few minutes alone with you?'

'Yes,' said Mrs. Gann. 'Soon.' She seemed to hug the child more closely for a moment, then eased her away. A pale, tear-lined face was ridged by the pattern of her mother's dress of lace at the throat; rich, white lace. 'Mimi,' Mrs. Gann said, 'You'll soon feel better, the mean man has gone away.'

58

'Has he—properly gone?'

'Yes, Mimi. Hasn't he, Mr. ——?'

'Yes, ma'am,' Whittaker said. 'I chased him, and he drove off in the car which was parked next door.'

'That's right,' said Mrs. Gann.

'I saw him come in the car,' Mimi announced. 'He went to the house next door first, Mummy.' She was looking with sharper interest at Whittaker, scrutinising him as if trying to assure herself that the big man with the strange voice was in fact a friend—and telling the truth.

Whittaker wondered what was passing through her mind.

'Did he nearly *kill* you?' she asked at last.

'Oh, it wasn't as bad as that,' said Whittaker. He spoke very slowly, articulating carefully, because he knew that the assumed voice was hard for a child to understand unless it was uttered slowly and distinctly. 'But he was a pretty bad man.'

'I could see that,' said Mimi. 'Just one look, and I could see.'

In five minutes she was almost completely herself. Still a little pale, but full of curiosity, lively for a five-year-old, with Bob Gann shining in her eyes and in her fair, wavy hair. Soon, Mrs. Gann was able to say:

'Why don't you go and play with your dolls, Mimi?'

'I don't want to play with my dolls.'

'Just you go along and play,' Mrs. Gann said, and laughed. That wasn't really forced. Whittaker could tell that she was giving thanks for the fact that the crisis was over, that Mimi was so nearly back to normal.

Mimi went out to the front lawn.

Mrs. Gann turned to face Whittaker for the first time, and he could not find words, could only look at her. Her eyes were questioning at first, but that changed; fright came into them. Face to face, he saw her simply as a beauty, and as a woman worthy of Bob Gann; of any man. She was nervous from reaction to the shock, and began to talk, too quickly. Her accent wasn't marked to Whittaker's ears, but was attractive.

'It's been such a morning,' she said. 'I hardly know how to say I'm sorry. I just felt too scared. I didn't know anything until that shot, and——' She broke off.

Whittaker said, 'It's all right, remember it's over.' He

was thinking: when she had come running towards him, and they had passed each other, she hadn't thought of anyone but her child.

'The neighbours were out,' she went on, still speaking too quickly: she gave the impression that she was trying to fend off some unseen thing. 'There's nobody nearer than Mrs. Pyne, and I guess she wouldn't hear anything—she's too far away. I'm so sorry that I——'

'Mrs. Gann,' Whittaker said in a flat voice, 'I can't stay here for long, but I wanted to tell you about this myself. It's not going to be good to hear.' He found words difficult, hard to find and as hard to utter. 'Will you sit down, please?'

He heard the child talking to a doll on the lawn, but was oblivious of that, oblivious of everything but Bob Gann's wife and the news that he had to give her.

He was conscious of another, strange feeling.

He was glad he had come; glad that he had not left this task to anyone else.

Slowly she sat down.

Fearfully, she waited.

CHAPTER VIII

THE TELLING

WHEN Whittaker began to speak again, Mrs. Gann looked as if she wanted to stop him, as if she would gladly shut her ears to words, as if she were badly frightened, and wanted to fight off the causes of fear. All that showed itself, as Whittaker watched her with great intentness, and as he said:

'I've brought bad news with me, Mrs. Gann, and I wish it could all be disposed of as easily as—as that man.' He didn't look away from her. 'Did he tell you that I travelled with Bob from England?'

Her right hand rose to her breast.

'No,' she said in a whisper.

'I had a lot in common with Bob, and he with me,' Whittaker went on. 'I used to be in the M.I.5 before I started to work on my own. Together we had a job to do on the ship coming from England. It didn't look particularly dangerous, but it seemed to be important. We had to watch over a man. We didn't like him much, but the voyage started without any sign of trouble, and it began to look as if were all a mistake.'

Whittaker paused again.

The woman's hands were raised, now, just above the level of her chin, as if to hide the fact that her lips began to quiver. Of course, she now *knew*; but still she wanted to fight, still she wanted to turn the inescapable aside.

'Last night,' Whittaker said, 'it boiled over. I was lucky. Bob wasn't. There's only one thing I can say that might help. It was quick, so quick that I doubt if he knew what was coming. I don't think he even suspected that death was on the way.'

There it was, the awful truth told.

Outside, Mimi was talking to her dolls, as if to human beings; scolding, loving, laughing, gay. Outside, the trees shaded the house and the windows from the sun, there was quietness and a beauty of its own. Outside, the world went on, and the people who had been alive yesterday were alive today. Somewhere was the hard-voiced man in the Chrysler, the killer who had run. There was the *Queen B.* alongside now, and Morrison with his three corpses and his thousands of impatient, restless, angry passengers, all with some special reason for favoured treatment.

In this house, he lived with tragedy.

Mrs. Gann's lips quivered and her hands were unsteady, and there was a shimmering pain in her eyes, as if the dawn itself were crying. Her face, touched by grief, had a starkness which impressed itself more deeply on his mind than any human face he had ever known. It would haunt him. Whenever he saw a woman, tall and deep-bosomed and with golden hair, he would think of what he was seeing now— the sheer, stark lines of beauty moulded by grief.

Then, very slowly and in a low voice, she said, 'Bob.'

That was all for a long time. Then:

'Bob,' she repeated.

Whittaker didn't speak. The child still talked and played, and he felt as if the only thing that could help this woman was prayer; and he did not know what kind of prayer would

61

help her. He wished that she would look away, he wished that he could wrench his gaze away from her; but he could not. They were there as if some compulsion made them look up on each other, so that he would never be in any doubt as to the measure of her hurt.

'*Bob, Bob, Bob,*' she said.

Whittaker made himself say: 'You can believe that, Mrs. Gann. He didn't know what was coming, couldn't have felt hurt.'

'Bob,' she repeated, like a sigh on an evening breeze.

Whittaker had no desire to move or speak, and had no way of helping her. He was still glad that he had come, that he had seen her before the news, before her desperate grief.

'Is there anyone I can send for?' he made himself say.

Slowly she shook her head.

He stood near her, and suddenly she leaned her head in her hands and began to cry; the sound seemed touched with the awfulness of despair. He stood with one hand on her shoulder. Outside, the child still played, unsuspecting. Nothing else had changed. Whittaker felt something of his own tension go, because he knew that this was why he had come; to be with her now.

*   *   *

Whittaker sat in the living-room, alone.

Nearly an hour had passed, and he was able to think of other things, including the fact that a gunman had been here, waiting for him. If anyone had reasoned so quickly that he would come straight here, the police might, too; in any case, they would soon be here and tell Mrs. Gann.

He kept watching the window and the road, but no one approached.

He couldn't keep his mind off Bob Gann's wife.

Without a word, she had eased herself out of her chair and gone out of the room, then come from the kitchen and turned up the wide, white-painted staircase, going slowly towards the room upstairs, holding onto the handrail as if afraid that without its help, she would fall. She hadn't looked round, and for a while it had seemed almost as if she had forgotten that Whittaker existed, as if she were wiping out all recollection of his visit. He had heard sounds of movement above his head, and the sounds from the child; and he had sat there, listening intently, half fearful that Mrs. Gann would do some desperate, fateful thing, yet believing that the child here and the young Bob he didn't know, would hold her back.

He couldn't stay.

The police could not wait much longer, would have to tell Mrs. Gann what had happened, and she would tell them that he had been here. Well, that wouldn't help them much, he could lose himself in New York, and he had come only to break the news to her.

The police would hear about the gunman; they would know he had come to kill Whittaker. That hard-voiced, vicious man with the coldness of death in his voice, had wanted to know what Pirran had told him, had been ready to kill to make sure he couldn't pass any knowledge on.

Whittaker looked up, suddenly.

He heard Mrs. Gann walking above his head, quite steadily; and this time she came out of a room, for he could hear a door open. She walked across the landing and started down the stairs. She approached quietly, not quickly nor slowly. Every movement she made had its own peculiar grace. She had beautiful legs; beautiful; and as her foot came down, the lines of the ankle moved with easy rhythm; then the other foot touched a lower step. It was like watching someone dancing, not walking.

She had washed her face, and put on powder, but no lipstick; that gave her a pallor which the silvery greyness of her eyes couldn't hide. Her arms were by her side, now, and she didn't hold on to the handrail. She reached the foot of the wide stairs, and said:

'I won't keep you waiting long.'

'There's no hurry,' he heard himself saying.

There was all the hurry in the world.

She went into the kitchen. He heard a sharp ting! and, a moment later, she spoke clearly:

'Hallo, Louise, is Mrs. Gardner there? . . . Yes, I'll wait for her, tell her it is Mrs. Gann.'

Silence.

Whittaker stood up, puzzled because Mimi had stopped talking. He went to the window. The venetian blinds were opened, so that he could see the green lawn, the trees with their silvery barks, the prams, the dolls, the shawls spread out, all the paraphernalia of the child's toys. Mimi herself was right at the end of the garden, poking at the ground with a stick, with that intentness which children show in the unusual. A red car came in sight.

Police? Whittaker's heart seemed to stop. No; the car swerved on the uneven road, and the driver waved to Mimi, who didn't seem to notice Whittaker.

'Elise, is that you?' Mrs. Gann said. 'Elise, I wonder if you would do me a big favour. . . . That's very kind of you, if you would have Mimi for the day, and Bob when he comes home from school. . . . Well, yes, it's bad news, Elise, but I can't talk about it right now. I don't want the children to know, yet. . . . Will you do that for me? . . . You're very kind, Elise, you don't know how much I appreciate it. I——'

She broke off, and seemed to catch her breath. The woman Elise obviously talked for a long time.

At last.

'Yes, it's Bob, but I just don't want to talk about it now. I have to—I have to go into New York to see—to see him.'

There was another pause, and then the softer ting of the telephone as she replaced it, a few moments of silence; and soon the sound was followed by the sight of her as she came towards Whittaker.

'Mimi will be going to a neighbour,' she said flatly, 'and I hope it will be convenient for me to come with you to the ship.' She had complete control of herself now, and there was not the slightest quiver in her voice. 'It won't take me long to get ready. I'll tell Mimi.' The only sign of her tension was the way she talked, almost without a pause, as if she dared not stop.

'No,' Whittaker said, 'I can't come with you, Mrs. Gann.'

She stopped in front of him.

'Why not?'

'You're going to find this hard to believe,' he said. 'I am on the run. Bob wasn't the only victim last night. There was a woman, too, and I had been in her cabin.' He watched the changing expressions on Mrs. Gann's face; she wasn't at all sure what to make of this, but there was one way in which he thought he could win her confidence completely. 'Bob was telling me of the time when he was after Nasaki. He told you about that.'

64

She followed his meaning at once, and said: 'He went on the run because it looked as if he had been guilty of taking bribes. He had to clear himself.' The understanding that Whittaker wanted to see dawned in her eyes. 'Is that how things are with you?'

'Exactly.'

'Why—why did you come here?'

Whittaker said: 'We were on the job together, Mrs. Gann, and I wanted to see it through—in all ways. I'm going to finish it off. I want to find who killed him. All I know now is that we were guarding Pirran, and Pirran is alive but Bob's dead. It's the kind of situation that won't let me sleep. I'd like to find all the answers, and I don't think I would have a chance if I were to give myself up.'

She was quiet for a long time.

'I'm beginning to think that anyone who could understand Bob could understand you,' she said at last. 'But I think you're wrong to attempt this.'

'What makes you think it?'

'You knew Bob for—five days.'

'Six,' corrected Whittaker; 'one and a half in England, four and a half on board the *Queen B*. It was long enough.'

'They killed him, and they killed others. They tried to kill you, here.'

'That's right,' said Whittaker softly, 'and they'll probably try again. I haven't really started to work this thing out, Mrs. Gann. I just know that I started the job and I'm going to finish it. That's how simple it is. I think I know how, too.'

She asked flatly, 'How?'

'I'll keep that to myself,' Whittaker said.

Mrs. Gann's lips twisted in what he knew was a smile, so wry, so painful, that it took a long time coming, but it came.

'I know what you mean,' she said. 'If I knew that, I would be in danger; that I would be vulnerable . . . well'— she drew a deep breath—'I don't know how vulnerable I am, but I'm going to spend all the time I have in finding out who killed Bob. From now on that's what I'm going to live for.' She stopped, but Whittaker thought that she could have added something which would make everything she said fall into place. She might have added, 'I don't think I shall feel alive again until they're caught.'

That was how she would react. . . .

For the first time it came to Whittaker that his coming here had been the finger which pointed their way, their way together, until they had found the killer of Bob Gann. He didn't know whether that was in her mind yet; it just came to him that it was inescapable. This was no brief meeting which would soon be forgotten. This was a beginning.

'I'm still not going to tell you how I mean to start,' Whittaker said. 'I'm on the run. Anyone with me will be, too. There's a job for a man, and this is mine; one for a woman, and Mimi and young Bob makes yours.'

'They'll stay with Bob's family in New Jersey,' Mrs. Gann announced. 'I shall take them tomorrow. And by tomorrow I should know a little more—about what the police say, for one thing.' That wry, painful smile came again. 'Do the police really think that you killed that woman?'

'If they do, I can't blame them. But I didn't.'

She asked quietly, 'You did not kill Bob, did you?'

'No,' he said, 'I didn't kill Bob.'

She said: 'Go to that window in the corner, will you, and watch? It's the only road to this house from Scarsdale. You'll get good warning if the police are coming.'

He said, 'Thanks, but I must go, I haven't much time.' He was adding to his danger every moment he stayed here.

'I won't be long,' she promised, and went out.

She went upstairs again. He stood near the window, able to see the road as it wound through wooded land, all gardens, and past houses which seemed a long way off.

He wished Gann's wife would hurry.

If he left her . . .

He couldn't leave her, don't be a fool.

She came hurrying at last, wearing a little hat and white gloves, ready to go out. There was no need to waste words.

'We'll take my car,' she said. 'We'll be away from Scarsdale in five minutes.'

She was commiting herself to helping Whittaker.

She drove him out of Scarsdale and to New York, finally onto the Henry Hudson parkway. The neighbour had come for Mimi and Gann's widow was going to Newark to arrange for Bob's parents to look after the children for the next few weeks. It was all said and done with that calm deliberation which Whittaker half admired, yet which in

66

some ways repelled him.

She would not really live again until full vengeance was done.

He wondered when he would see her again.

He wondered if he would ever see her without the thought and shadow of vengeance in her eyes.

CHAPTER IX

THE LAMPREY HOTEL

WHITTAKER put the Master-at-Arms' uniform into the cardboard box in which he had brought his linen clothes away, tied it up, and checked it at Grand Central Station. he posted the key to the *Queen B*, where it would be delivered next day. He bought a beige skull-cap with a wide peak at a Five and Ten Cent Store, which sold goods of all prices up to a hundred dollars, and an overnight bag in which he could put all the oddments he had with him.

That took him all the morning. He was as sure of himself and his anonymity as a man could be. He had used his great asset before. A droop of one shoulder, a curve at one lip, the dull eyes, and above all the voice which aroused no comment at all, would see him through.

Well, it should. . . .

By mid-day it was so hot that everyone on the streets looked ready to drop. No one hurried. The traffic moved at a slower rate. The traffic cops got bad-tempered, whistled, shrilled, and men bellowed. The stench of petrol fumes seemed to fill every corner of every street. The throbbing heart of the city beat a little less fiercely than usual, and seemed to have a sluggish note of anger. The one relief came inside the shops, where the air-conditioning brought coolness, but there was also the dread of going out into the humid heat of the streets.

By two o'clock, when Whittaker left a drug store where he had a sandwich and ice-cream, the heat seemed to strike at him. His coat was damp at the collar and his shirt stuck to his back.

67

With the peak pulled low over his eyes, ostensibly and reasonably against the sun, most of his face was in shadow; an added security.

No one took the slightest notice of him, not even to get out of his path. No one seemed remotely interested in anything except getting through the day. At the newspaper stands, the placards talked of UNO, of Murder, of Murder Aboard the *Queen B.*, but even that couldn't stir up interest.

Whittaker bought a *Daily Mirror*, whose placards and headlines shrieked the loudest, but didn't stand reading it, just put it under his arm. He took a bus from Broadway at 46th Street, and sat down as the doors hissed to and the driver glowered when he asked for change. He got off at a stop near 85th Street. The crowds were thinner here, but just as limp.

The Lamprey Hotel, where Olive Johns and Maisie Gregson were to have stayed, was only just on Broadway. In fact, a corner of it was; the entrance was some distance along 61st Street, with its tall houses, its grey sidewalks. It looked dark inside, and also cool. He went in, carrying his case; no porter was waiting. A dozen armchairs stood about, a uniformed boy lounged at the door of an open elevator, there was a brown carpet, the place was as cool as it looked. A door led to a snack bar, a flight of narrow stairs led upwards, out of sight.

A girl sat at the reception desk, with a book open in front of her. The Register was open, too, facing Whittaker. He didn't glance at it; if Olive Johns were coming here, she wouldn't arrive until the police had cleared the *Queen B.*, and that certainly wouldn't be until later today.

The girl was not only big but blonde, amiable-looking, cushiony.

'You want something?'

'Do you have a room?'

'For one person?'

'Sure.'

'For how long, mister?'

'Maybe a week, maybe two.'

'You like it high, or you like it low?'

'I like it in between,' he said, and grinned.

'Sure,' the girl nodded. 'Register, please, and you can take a look at two or three rooms, the bell-boy will show you.

68

Anyone still alive outside?'

'To look at them,' Whittaker said, 'no.'

She gave a rather nice smile, with big white teeth and bright red lips.

He signed as P. E. White, and when the girl called the bell-boy over, handing him the keys, she said:

'Hope you find one of them to your liking, Mr. White.'

'I'm sure I will.'

'Just let me know.'

'Sure,' said Whittaker.

When he reached the lift, she wasn't looking at him, which meant that she had not found him out of the ordinary. Well, why should she? If he didn't make any major mistake, he would get through. If he hadn't felt sure of himself, he dared not have tried.

He had seen no police, but it was early for them to get round to the hotel, wasn't it?

He couldn't be sure; just had to be careful.

The coloured boy was bright and eager in his smart, puce uniform.

'De best room is Forty-eight, sah, ah'm sure yo'll agree about that,' he said. 'On de fourth floor, and with a good window which oberlook both ways. That seem right to yo', sah?'

'It sounds fine.'

'This way,' the boy said.

The window had a bay. One side of the bay showed Whittaker Broadway, with a cake-shop and a delicatessen just in sight; the other bay showed him the stretch of blue water of the Hudson River; it shimmered in the sun, two or three blocks away. Traffic on the parkway flashed by, like vari-coloured beetles being chased by vari-coloured beetles in an unending stream. The room was a fair size, with a double bed, a corner partitioned off with the bath, shower, everything he needed. The two armchairs looked comfortable.

'Sure, I'll have this,' he said.

'Okay, sah,' said the boy. 'I'll tell Miss Mary.'

'Thanks. Do that.' Whittaker took the room key, and put fifty cents into the gloved hand: it was the right tip, as much as the boy expected and enough to make him flash his teeth. He went out and closed the door.

Whittaker put his case on the bed, and then moved to the window. He stood looking out for several minutes. Traffic slid by; he could hear the whine of buses as they stopped and started up just round the corner. There was a flower-shop in sight, too, and a milliner's, with a dozen hats on show. A few people drooped past. Some children looked almost spritely, as if they didn't care about the weather. Whittaker realised that it was pleasantly cool in the room, and that anyone who knew the Lamprey Hotel knew value.

He turned away, and opened the *New York Daily Mirror*.

There it was: the whole story, as far as the Press could get it, and the simple fact that the police wanted to find Neil Whittaker. There was no picture of him, or the man he had killed, but there was one of Bob Gann, and there was one of Maisie Gregson; a beauty, too; she looked sweet and even innocent! The story half suggested that it wouldn't be long before sensations developed; the fact that Gann had served the F.B.I. was a guarantee of that.

Whittaker put the paper aside.

For a while he wanted just to think; to try to get everything crystal clear in his mind; to work out the essentials as he saw them, to check that he was right in thinking that the quickest way to results was to have a long talk with Olive Johns in the hope that she could tell him where to find Pirran.

He *must* find Pirran; and apart from the man at Scarsdale, Olive was the one possible informant.

He hadn't much time. He had to explain facts which were only just becoming obvious. Pirran surely hadn't been really nervous on board the *Queen B.*, whatever nervousness he had shown before. He had tried every trick he knew to have company for the night.

What had caused that change of mood?

The two women themselves?

Whittaker's mind switched from them to the man at Scarsdale; to talk of a packet, and to fear of what Pirran might have told Gann and Whittaker.

Whittaker finished his cigarette.

A shower and a change of clothes would give him a good start. He could check from time to time if Olive Johns registered here. He could seek ways of finding out where Pirran went after he left the *Queen B.* A Stop Press in the

Mirror said that the passengers were still being detained but that it was hoped that they would all be ashore by dinner-time.

That was about right, Whittaker thought . . . if they were lucky.

He went for the shower.

*   *   *

He sat in one of the armchairs in the corner in the entrance hall, away from the reception desk. There was another door which led into a restaurant, dark and hushed on the other side of the hall; he had a steak there which was surely the steak of a century.

Two or three people had come in, but no one else had signed on. Mary the girl with big white teeth and full red lips, still spread her amplitude, and read her book. Whittaker had a newspaper on his knees, ready to raise it if there should be the slightest need.

The swing doors opened again.

A little woman came in, breathing hard, looking as if she would drop. Her forehead was wet and streaked with damp, grey hair. She fanned her damp face with a newspaper as she plodded towards the desk. Something about her attracted Whittaker's attention, and he didn't notice the man come in until he was halfway to the desk.

Whittaker put the paper up, quickly.

He was having luck. The hard-voiced man who had waited for him at Mrs. Gann's was striding after the woman.

He caught her up just before she reached the desk, and stretched out his hand to the girl sitting there. He didn't speak. She didn't, either, but took a key off a hook and dropped it into his hand, her fingers crooked, as if to make sure that she shouldn't touch him.

He grunted and turned away.

He was less than medium height, thin enough to be ugly, with deep-set eyes, a swarthy skin, and a nervous springy kind of walk. He went to the unattended elevator and the doors slid to behind him.

Whittaker lowered the newspaper.

Something which had been frozen in him, since he had first seen the back of Gann's head, began to melt now. This was a start; this was the place from which he could go a long way. There was no hurry. He didn't believe in coincidence to the degree that this man would come by chance to the Lamprey Hotel.

The cushiony girl dealt smoothly with the hot and flustered woman.

Whittaker got up and sauntered across to the desk, money jangling in his hand; by the girl's side were stacks of cigarettes and a wire rack filled with twenty-five cent books, mostly salacious, sexy or sadistic, if the pictures could be believed.

'You keep *Pall Mall*?' he asked.

'Sure.' She had to go beneath the desk for the big red packet of *Pall Malls*. 'Why don't you buy yourself a whole pack, mister, and save yourself a quarter?'

'That's exactly how I'll buy them from this day on.'

She slid a long box of two hundred cigarettes towards him, and he gave her a five-dollar bill. She fiddled for change. He watched the movement of her long, white arm and her snugly filled white blouse.

'That man who came in a few minutes ago,' he said, 'he reminded me of a guy I don't like at all.'

She said, 'He reminds me of a guy I don't like, too.'

'That so? He a regular?'

'He booked in this morning. It won't break my heart if he books out tonight.'

'He wouldn't be my guy, would he?' Whittaker asked. 'Name of Karney?'

'I don't know what his name is,' she said, 'but here he calls himself Blick.'

'Blick?'

'There,' she said, and stabbed a finger at the entry immediately above Whittaker's; and she told him everything he wanted to know. 'David Blick,' he had signed in an untidy hand, 'from Kenton, New Jersey. Room 34.'

'Thanks,' Whittaker said. 'Not my man; just too bad.'

He sauntered back to his chair and sat down. He had no objection to waiting, because he was quite clear in his mind what he was going to do, and he didn't feel in any great hurry about it.

It was ten o'clock when Olive Johns arrived.

She came by taxi, she had a heap of luggage, and another coloured porter sprang to action when he knew that. She looked tired. Her demureness was still there, but it was badly jaded. Her hair, under a silly little hat, looked as if she hadn't given it any serious attention today. Her nose was shiny, and her shoulders drooped.

Whittaker waited.

She was given room 35, booked by letter by Maisie.

'I hope you'll be comfortable,' said the girl clerk. 'Will Miss Gregson be coming, Miss Johns?'

Olive Johns said flatly, 'She won't be coming.'

'That's all right,' the clerk said; 'the room will be fine for one person.'

Whittaker watched the porter open the elevator door, and then heard the squeal of brakes outside. There was no crash, but there was a lot of shouting. That stopped. The revolving doors opened, and a little man appeared, breathing very hard.

'What's going on out there?' the clerk asked.

'Two guys and a fight,' the little man said. 'You'd think it was too hot.' He grinned, and went to the door leading to the restaurant.

Whittaker stood up.

He went to the stairs, and started up them with long strides; and the bell-boy, Sam, saw him and looked astounded as if he didn't expect to see any resident walking *up* stairs. Whittaker winked. He reached the third floor, and reached room 34—Blick's room. It was next door to room 35—the girl's; the two cream-painted doors were close together in a narrow passage. Somewhere, a radio or a television was on, with a musical. Whittaker went to the nearest corner.

He hadn't to wait long.

The lift stopped, the doors opened with a hiss which travelled all along the passage. Then came footsteps, the girl's and the porter's. Whittaker didn't look round, but the voices told him all he wanted to know; with the help of an opening door, the thump as if cases were being put down heavily.

The porter said, 'I'll be right back, miss, with the other trunks.'

'Thank you,' Olive Johns said in that flat, lifeless voice.

The porter went off.

A door closed.

Whittaker shifted to a position where he could see the two

73

doors. Number 34 didn't open; he doubted if it would until
the rest of the luggage was up here. It came in less than ten
minutes, and this time when the door closed there was a kind
of finality about it; the silence which followed seemed
absolute.

Whittaker could see but not be seen unless someone
stared hard along this way.

He waited for perhaps five minutes; long enough to
wonder whether he had been wrong, and whether the long
arm of coincidence had stretched out.

It had not.

The door of room 34 opened, and next moment the man
named Blick tapped at the door of the adjoining room. A
faint sound followed, as if Olive Johns were calling out,
'Who is it?' The man answered in a rounded voice, rather
like the bell-boy's, 'It's the bell-boy, ma'am.'

His hands were out of his pocket; Whittaker saw that, so
he didn't stop Blick from going in. He heard the door open.
He heard the sharp exclamation from the girl, clear enough
to betray its rising note of fear. Then Blick moved, swiftly,
with the kind of movements he would make if he were
grabbing the girl to keep her quiet and to thrust her into
the room. He followed, with a flurrying sound.

The door slammed.

Whittaker moved, and was outside it almost before it had
stopped quivering. Without losing a second, he selected a
skeleton key from the bunch in his hip pocket, and used it
swiftly, nimbly. Sounds from inside the room drowned any
he was making.

He opened the door a fraction.

He heard Blick say: 'You can have it the hard way, or
you can have it easy, sister. Pirran gave you a packet, and
that's the packet I've come here for.'

'I tell you he didn't give me anything!'

'Isn't that too bad?' Blick sneered. There was a sharp
sound; the kind that would come if her face was being
slapped. 'Don't give me more trouble, sister. Which case
is it in?'

'I don't—I don't know what you're talking about,'
Olive Johns said hoarsely. 'Honestly, I don't.'

'Give me that,' said Blick; and Whittaker heard faint
sounds, believed that the man had snatched her handbag.

He heard a footstep, as if Blick had backed away a pace. There was the sound of heavy breathing, but nothing else. Other little noises followed, which Whittaker couldn't make out.

He opened the door wider and stepped into the room. Neither of the others saw him.

Blick stood with his back to him, almost hiding Olive. He was tossing things about the room. A compact hit the wall and dropped heavily, powder billowing out. A purse struck the arm of a chair and burst open, showering coins into the chair and on the floor. A lipstick lodged neatly in a drawer in the dressing-table which was open an inch or so.

Then Blick swung the empty handbag round, to strike the girl's face. She dodged. In her alarm she didn't see Whittaker, but once on the move she went more quickly. The door of the bathroom was open, all she could think of was getting there, for Blick blocked her way to the passage door. Sobbing, she turned and ran towards it, but Blick was quick. He didn't get there first, but slid out a leg, and she tripped. She flung her arms out to save herself, and both her hands struck the bathroom door with a hollow boom. Then she fell and Blick raised a foot viciously.

'Must you?' inquired Whittaker mildly.

Blick's foot wavered.

The girl didn't hear the words, but Blick did. He turned round, gaping, and as he moved, his right hand was moving towards his pocket with rattlesnake speed. He wouldn't trouble to draw, but would fire through the pocket of his snug-fitting brown coat.

Whittaker didn't give him the chance, but moved and swung his right arm. His fist caught Blick on the side of the jaw. It was probably the first time that anyone had hit Blick so hard that he was lifted clean off the floor. His feet actually left the carpet, and he pitched sideways; a chair got between him and the wall, or he would probably have died in much the way of the stranger on the *Queen B.* staircase. As it was, his body concertina'd into the armchair, and had no time to straighten out before Whittaker reached it.

Whittaker grabbed at waving legs.

He gripped the ankles tightly and lifted Blick up by them. Blick hadn't even started to recover from the blow, and probably did not realise what was happening to him.

Whittaker held him high and swung him to and fro, so that his hair hung down and touched the floor, but his head didn't touch it, he wasn't actually hurt. Things began to fall from his pocket; a wallet, a key, a small automatic pistol with a short thick rubber silencer attached, more, smaller keys, a comb. Whittaker kept swinging Blick, and the arc seemed to grow a little wider until, at moments, Blick was almost horizontal with the floor. He kept making little bleating noises, but he was probably not fully conscious.

Whittaker swung him towards the armchair and let him go. He collapsed into it and crumpled up, quivering like a chicken after it had lost its head.

Whittaker turned to the girl.

The white heat of his own rage had gone, and he could begin to think about her. She was on her knees with her hands on the floor, staring up at him. Obviously she had started to get up, seen what was happening, and just hadn't been able to move.

'All right, Olive,' said Whittaker. 'He won't hurt you again. He won't hurt anyone else for a long time.' He went to her, and she raised one hand, as if that were as much as she could do. He helped her to her feet. She wasn't trembling now, but seemed struck dumb. With an ineffectual motion she first straightened out her skirt, then began to poke her fingers through her hair, which wasn't anything like as untidy as it might have been.

Her face was dusky red, but the blood was draining from it, leaving her pale.

He remembered her as he had seen her in his bed. . . .

'Sit down,' he said, 'and take it easy.'

She went unsteadily to another chair, and sat down. He hadn't anything to offer her, so went across to Blick and felt his hip pocket. He wasn't disappointed.

He unscrewed the cap of a leather flask and sniffed.

'Rye,' he said. 'You won't like it, but it will set the corpuscles on fire. Take a sip.'

She took one and proved him wrong; she didn't mind it at all and took a second and a third sip. He moved the flask away, and screwed the cap on. Blick was collapsed in the chair like a punctured balloon, his body gradually assuming

76

a more normal position. His head rested on the back of the chair, one arm hung over the arm, one leg was doubled up beneath him, the other drooped to the carpet. His eyes were closed and his mouth slack.

'Better?' Whittaker asked Olive.

'Yes, I—thanks.'

'As they say in this new world, you're welcome. Did Pirran give a packet to you or Maisie?'

She said, 'I don't know about Maisie, but he didn't give one to me.'

'Did he talk about a packet?'

'No.'

'Did he give you anything?'

'Yes,' she said; 'a few drinks and a few passes.' She was much better, with a more healthy colour; almost pert. 'You—you're Whittaker?' She made it sound almost unbelievable.

'That's right.'

'The police——' She simply didn't finish.

'Want me,' Whittaker said for her. 'Yes, they do, Olive. One of their mistakes. This chap Blick is the one they really ought to interview, but I don't know whether we can persuade them of that. Until I feel sure about them I shall keep in a safe place. Olive——'

'Yes?'

'Remember our little *tête-à-tête* last night?'

'I . . . Yes.' She moistened her lips.

'Remember what you wore?'

She was looking at him narrowly, tensely. He didn't think that embarrassment really had anything to do with her expression or her heightened colour—that was probably the rye—but he could be wrong.

'I remember,' she said.

'Why did you go to my cabin?'

'It was——' She didn't go on.

'Look,' Whittaker said earnestly, 'I shan't try the Blick treatment on you, but I shall get at the truth. It's my general idea to be helpful, but you'll have to co-operate. Repeat: why did you go to my cabin?'

She said, 'It was Camponi's idea.'

'Who is Camponi?'

77

'He was killed last night,' she said shakily. 'He killed Maisie and Bob Gann; then someone——' She couldn't finish.

Blick stirred and Whittaker glanced at him. Both the man's feet were drooping over the chair, and he was sitting there as if quite normally, with his eyes partly open and his mouth no longer slack. He offered no threat for the next five minutes, except that he had ears. Whittaker moved towards him and he hardly blinked. Whittaker hesitated, then looked at the girl.

'Do you have any cotton wool?'

'There's—there's some in my handbag.'

Whittaker let her get it. She tried no tricks and pulled no gun. He rolled two small balls of cotton wool and pressed them into Blick's ears; the man made only a grunting protest, was vaguely aware of what was happening.

Whittaker turned back to Olive.

'So his name was Camponi; he killed Bob Gann and Maisie, and you took his orders.' His voice was hard and cold.

Olive said thinly helplessly: 'I didn't know what he was doing. He—he had a hold over me.'

'What kind of hold?'

She closed her eyes.

'I'd—I'd killed a man. Oh, I didn't mean to; it was really—really an accident. But he died. Camponi knew. He was a friend of Maisie's—lived with her in London when he was there; when he wasn't home, Maisie and I shared a flat.'

She was making sense.

Whittaker said, 'Keep going, Olive.'

'All right,' she said wearily, 'all right. Maisie and I were on board to make a fool of Pirran. There was a packet, wrapped in brown paper and sealed—and we had to get it.

'We—we couldn't.

'Pirran pretended to be a lecherous old man, but he wasn't really, and most certainly he wasn't a fool. But Camponi kept pressing us to get that packet, and when the last night at sea came, he got desperate.

'He—he thought Maisie could get into Pirran's cabin that night, and Maisie had fixed Pirran's drink so that he would drop off into a drugged sleep. He knew one of you would be watching and told me to go to your room and keep you there. How I hated it!'

It was almost possible to be sorry for her.

'Go on,' Whittaker said stonily.

She closed her eyes for a moment, then went on slowly:

'I didn't know what happened until afterwards, when he came and released me. He was absolutely crazy. He'd found a packet, but it was empty. He didn't say what he expected to find; just said he had to get the real one, and that—that he'd kill Bob Gann and would kill you. And—he would have done. So would Blick. Blick's a friend of his; I saw him in England once.'

Whittaker said quietly, 'Take it easy, Olive.' He gave her another drink and she gulped it down. Gasping a little, she went on. 'While you were out he came to your cabin to kill you, and heard me. I managed to bang the door a little. He let me out and kept saying that he'd come to kill you. He seemed—*mad*.'

'Because he'd got the wrong packet?'

'Yes.'

'Did he tell you he had killed Maisie?'

'He—he said he'd teach her to double-cross him. He thought she'd made a deal with Pirran, but——'

'Had she?'

'I don't know!' Olive cried.

Whittaker didn't speak at once. If he had to bet on her, it would be that she had told the truth; but he wasn't sure she had told all of it. Blick believed that she had that mystery packet which was so important that the dead Camponi had lost his head, his nerve and his life over it.

A lot of questions were answered.

If Whittaker judged Olive right, she couldn't take any more punishment now, so he didn't try to give her any. He picked up the room key which he had shaken from Blick's pocket and handed it to her.

She looked puzzled.

'It's number thirty-four—next door,' he said. 'Go and sit back in there for ten minutes. I'll join you soon. Don't try to run off, or the police will want to know why.'

She started to get up.

'All right, but'—she hesitated. 'Can I have another drink?'

Whittaker said, 'Something's corroding you, Olive, and it

could be whisky.' He handed her the flask, and a minute later watched her go out. He knew that she might be listening at the door, so he waited for two minutes, studying Blick all the time, then he went silently to the door and opened it abruptly.

Olive wasn't there.

Whittaker locked the door and turned to Blick. He didn't speak as he took out the ear-plugs. He was not only physically powerful; there was a hardness in his expression which Blick undoubtedly recognised. Ruthlessness looked the same in any man. Whittaker raised his hands and bunched them. He seemed to tower over Blick; and even if Blick had been standing, Whittaker would have been inches taller.

He said, 'I could tear you apart.'

Blick didn't speak, just moistened his lips and looked as if he would like to shrink further away.

'And it wouldn't take long,' Whittaker said.

Blick muttered, 'I——' but couldn't go on.

'Who sent you to me at Mrs. Gann's?' asked Whittaker, without raising his voice. 'Remember, I want the answer, and if I don't get it fast I'll hit you. And this time I'll hit hard.'

Blick said: 'No, don't do it! I——'

'Who sent you to Scarsdale?'

'Listen,' Blick said, and his expression was pitiful; his voice was so hoarse that the words seemed to run into each other. 'I don't know why they sent me. Ricky sent me. He— he thought you might turn up there.' Blick gulped. 'He had a nose in a newspaper office who told him you'd escaped.'

'Hurry!' Whittaker urged harshly.

'I—I could run into big trouble with Ricky,' Blick muttered, and looked as if he were really afraid of the man behind the name. 'He told me I was to find out what you knew about Pirran. And when I thought I'd got it all, I had to——'

He stopped again.

'A rub out?' Whittaker demanded.

Blick made a movement of his head; it wasn't enough to be called a nod.

'You had to find out what Pirran had told me?' Whittaker echoed. 'You mean, you had to find out if I knew what was in that packet and where it was?'

Blick gasped.

'Yes, yes, that's it!'

'Don't shout!' warned Whittaker, and went on:

'Where can I find Ricky?'

Blick cried:

'*I don't know!*'

'Blick,' said Whittaker softly, 'I've never known a man ask for trouble the way you do.' He clenched his fist again and moved forward, and his expression told Blick what to expect.

'I daren't give Ricky away,' Blick almost sobbed; 'I'd be——'

He stopped.

The telephone bell rang.

It was so unexpected that it made Whittaker slew round and stare. The telephone was on a table beside the bed, and the chair in which Blick sat was by the window. The head of the bed was against the wall opposite the window. Whittaker moved round, watching Blick all the time, knowing that the man had recovered enough to try to get away.

This was Olive's room, remember; not his.

He lifted the telephone.

'Hallo,' he said, 'who's that?' And it might have been a man named White talking.

A girl spoke briskly, laconically.

'If you're a friend of Miss Johns, okay—you can tell her that the cops are on their way up to see her. I'm just giving her time to think it over.'

'Thanks,' said Whittaker. 'You're a real friend.'

The line went dead, the girl at the desk had done her good deed. It was a deed which Blick didn't know about. The police would come here and open the door and find him in the middle of the mess he had made. There was only one snag; that he might run in time.

Whittaker said, 'If you ever get out of jail, give my love to Ricky.' He moved; and before the terrified man could dodge, struck him again on the side of the chin.

Blick would be out of this world for minutes, at least; the police would have plenty of time to wait for him.

Whittaker went to the door.

He opened it and stepped into the passage; and as he did so the elevator door whined open, and he knew that the police were only just round the corner.

CHAPTER X

RUN

WHITTAKER heard a door open just behind him; the door of Blick's room. He stepped backwards, ready for anything that Olive could do. All she did was to make room for him, and close the door. She leaned against it. There was something akin to desperation in her eyes, and she looked young— *very young*. He stared at her as the police tramped along the passage, and as one man knocked heavily against the door of the next room.

She *was* young.

She had made up too much aboard the *Queen B.*, and he had taken it for granted that she was as old as she looked. Until the night of the murders, he had not really studied her. Now, he saw that she was probably still in her teens; at most, twenty-one or -two. Her lips were unsteady, and she seemed to want to say something that wouldn't come out.

'Why—why are those policemen next door?' she whispered.

They were opening the door—it crashed back against the wall, and the sound spoke for itself. Men's voices were raised, in surprise and perhaps in shock, at sight of Blick.

'They wanted to see you,' Whittaker said flatly.

'They—they questioned me for hours on the ship. I—I'm so scared,' she said, and now he believed that the few minutes on her own had put fear into her. Time to reflect was time to panic. 'Don't—don't let them start on me again.'

'What particular thing will they start on, Olive?'

'Questions, questions, questions.' She actually shivered. 'The same questions you've asked. Did Maisie get anything

82

from Pirran, and—*I simply don't know.*' She kept her voice on a low key and kept glancing towards the wall which separated her from the police. 'I tell you I just don't know.'

'But they think you might, just as Blick does.'

'If Maisie knew anything, she didn't tell me!'

'All right,' said Whittaker, 'I hope that's true. Now listen. The New York police aren't so tough or so rough as you think. They won't manhandle you. And if you get really scared, remind them that you're a British citizen and ask for help from the Consulate. You'll get it. You may get even more than you deserve,' he added sardonically. 'And when the police do start questioning you, tell them what you know about the voyage.'

'I have,' she said, almost piteously. 'I tell you I have! It's just the—the old affair I'm scared about.'

Even if he wanted to, there wasn't a thing Whittaker could do to help her about that; and he wasn't sure that he wanted to. He thought it possible that the police would tell her that she couldn't stay in New York and would ship her back to Southampton; but that was guessing. The hard fact remained: police were in the room next door, and the moment they set eyes on him he would be neck-deep in trouble.

'Olive,' he said suddenly, 'do you have any money?'

'You mean—dollars?'

'Yes.'

'I've only about a hundred—Maisie gave them to me,' Olive said; 'she was going to give me more when we got here. I can't stay more than a few days.'

Whittaker took out his wallet, selected two hundreds and handed them to her. She looked bewildered, but took them. She stared at the notes, then at Whittaker: at last she tucked the notes into the shallow V of her blouse. She swallowed hard; he could see the muscles of her neck working. He hoped that the gift would pay dividends some time in the future, and if they didn't there wasn't a thing he could do about it.

'Be a good girl,' he said. 'Now I'm going.'

The sounds in the passage had quietened; men were talking in the next room. Olive moved. Whittaker opened the door cautiously. The other room door was open, but no one was in sight.

He couldn't stay in Blick's room in case that was searched.

He stepped into the passage and started to close the door. There were ten yards between him and the corner, and the odds were on him making them before anyone came out of the girls' room.

He started with a long stride.

Then a door opened, nearly opposite Olive John's room, and a policeman appeared behind him.

Whittaker didn't try to hide from the fact; he was in as tight a jam as he'd ever known. As he had run, he had made the case against him as black as it could be. He heard the policeman shout: 'Here he is, boys! Watch yourselves.'

The policeman had a gun, but wasn't in the right position to shoot.

Whittaker had Blick's automatic but didn't try to use it.

Other men moved fast. Whittaker didn't see them, but guessed that they came tearing out of the room into the passage. He rounded the corner, knowing that the policeman behind him was approaching swiftly. If that wasn't bad enough he found another New York cop in front. This man's hand was at his revolver, his feet were planted wide apart, guarding the doors of the elevator. These were closed. The cop looked broad and tough and his gun looked deadly.

'Just hold it,' he said. 'Don't rush me, son.'

More men came hurrying from behind Whittaker, and there wasn't any doubt that they would be armed and ready to shoot.

'Okay,' Whittaker said and forced a grin. 'I won't make any trouble.' He stopped moving and his voice sounded tired. He was three yards away from the armed policeman ahead, and the others were almost on top of him. He leaned against the wall and held his hands high in token of surrender, as two men in plain clothes swung towards him.

One exclaimed, 'It's Whittaker!'

'Just call me Neil,' said Whittaker in that tired voice. 'And ask your friend to put away his gun, will you? I get nervous of people with guns.'

'I can think of another way of making you nervous,' said the second plain-clothes man. He was big and tall, almost another Bob Gann; he was Bob's type, too. He eyed Whittaker up and down, and the uniformed policeman waited for instructions, while the first plain-clothes man, gun in hand, moved towards Whittaker.

'Watch him,' he said.

'Don't crowd me,' Whittaker said. 'There's no need.'

He saw all three of them, yet nothing was clearer than the face of Bob Gann's wife, which was in his mind's eye even then. He knew that she was going out for vengeance, and was sure that nothing would stop her from trying. He didn't think that by herself she stood a chance in a thousand. If he were caught and taken to the police headquarters, it would reach the Press, and the Press would spread it over the front pages. He couldn't gag them even if he wanted to. It would take a long time to get a friendly word from New Scotland Yard—and that might not help much when it came; it would take plenty of time to persuade the New York police to believe his story.

It would take much too long.

The three men were drawing closer, warily, as if they expected him to make a fight, and could guess what that fight could do to them. They had seen Blick, and they had seen the man on the stairs of the *Queen B.* with his broken neck. Only fools would be careless, and these men weren't fools.

Whittaker coughed.

He put a hand to his chest suddenly, and twisted his face as if he were in acute pain. Then he leaned back against the wall, gasping. The uniformed policeman drew back, one of the others stopped with his hand outstretched. The man who reminded Whittaker of Bob Gann said sharply:

'Who are you trying to fool?'

Whittaker said, 'No fooling.' He screwed up his face again, clenched his hands and held his body rigid, as if he were in agony. They weren't sure of him; wary but worried. He began to crumple up, knees sagging, head drooping, and he made a noise in his throat. Some of these men had heard that noise before; anyone who had heard death come to a human being had heard that kind of rattle.

Whittaker, eyes open and head lowered, saw their legs and feet, saw the way they stopped, could imagine the sense of horror in them. There was a gap between the two plain-clothes men—and through the gap, the staircase.

He was bent almost double.

Then he sprang, the only way he could, thrusting his lean body forward with his hands outstretched. He heard the exclamations, but didn't know whether he had won the respite he needed. He put one hand flat on the floor and turned head-over-heels in a handspring which carried him to the stairs. His body swerved downwards. He saw the stairs looming up, got both hands down again and somersaulted, and that brought him to a turn in the stairs. He landed on one foot, and for a split second feared a twisted ankle or a twisted knee; anything that might hold him here. He knew that once they had sight of him they would shoot; they weren't taught to take this kind of desperation lying down, and had good reason to believe that they were dealing with a killer.

He glanced up and saw a gun, a hand and a foot.

He jumped down the next half-flight of stairs. A shot roared, and in the confined space it was like a cannon going off. Chippings from the wall showered about his head. He leapt the next half-flight of stairs, and then luck first threatened and next swung round in his favour. A huge carton filled with rubbish stood on the landing and nearly trapped him. He evaded it, stood by for a second and then grabbed the carton and tilted it, then tipped it over. The police were running down the stairs. They would run into the rubbish and the box, and he would gain seconds; but seconds might not be enough.

Down again. . . . One flight of stairs to go.

Footsteps sounded like thunder.

He didn't tempt fate, but ran down these. The bottom landing was larger, there was carpet on the floor, and the door which led to the lift also led to the hall. He drew a deep breath and thrust them open. He saw one lift standing empty, the doors of another closed; and they might open at any moment, letting the police spill out. He didn't run but strode across the hall, startling a little man who had taken over from the blonde at the desk. He also startled a family, just coming in, cursing them under his breath. A man dodged out of his way. The elevator door stayed closed, and no one burst through the other doorway.

Whittaker thrust the double doors open, and stepped into the street.

Heat struck at him.

No one was in sight, right or left, except on Broadway. There a stream of cars snarled past traffic lights. Immediately opposite the Lamprey Hotel was a gap in the parked cars, and he went through this. He heard the whine of a bus on Broadway and broke into a run: no one was surprised to see a man running for a bus. As he reached the corner it stopped to let a woman get off. He leapt for it. He didn't know whether anyone else had come from the hotel yet. He jumped aboard and had hardly taken a step before the driver closed the doors and started off, jolting Whittaker forward to beat the lights. Whittaker twisted his head. Men streamed out of the hotel as the bus passed; 'streamed', looked right; there were three of them at least, and they seemed to spill into the street. They stopped, as men on the hunt will stop, to look right and left. They split up, one coming towards Broadway, the other towards the opposite corner.

The bus carried Whittaker out of sight.

There was plenty of room. He dropped into a seat and let himself flop there, his chest heaving. He sensed the curiosity of other passengers, but didn't give them a serious thought or a glance. His mind began to work again. The hue-and-cry would have been great enough before, and it would be doubled now. New York was so hot for him that he dare not be recognised moving about the streets. Hotels and restaurants would be danger-spots.

But he had a lot to do in New York, and had to find a hide-out.

There was a break in his thoughts. He peered out at the signs on the lamp-posts at the street corners and saw 77th Street sign. Eight streets on, eight *blocks* on, and one or two west, and he would be at the apartment of Mrs. Gann's sister, Riverside Drive at 85th Street. In the present darkness he had some security, the real heat wouldn't be on until the morning.

The next bus-stop would be nearest 85th Street.

He got off.

The street was wider than most, this seemed some kind of a traffic junction. Cars were streaming both in and out of the city which never slept. There were more lights, more open shops, more people walking. Windows everywhere were open and people sat at most of them. Men walked in their shirt sleeves, women in flimsy dresses, all seeking the illusory coolness of the night.

He turned off Broadway without hurrying.

No sirens screamed.

It wasn't until he reached Riverside Drive with its tall grey houses and its gardens between the houses and the Parkway, that he felt that he was breathing normally. He had a sense of exhilaration, too, the feeling that came when the breaks went his way.

He looked for the apartment.

It didn't occur to him that he could throw his hand in, give himself up, be sure of a clearance from Scotland Yard. The sense of excitement as he reached the house and went inside increased.

Deep down, he knew that it was because he might see Mrs. Gann again—now.

CHAPTER XI

NEWS OF PIRRAN

A WOMAN opened the door. It wasn't Mrs. Gann, but obviously she was related. There was the same corn-coloured hair, the same clear skin, the same kind of figure: Mrs. Gann in miniature. She stood with her body outlined against the light, and it seemed almost strange to Whittaker to know that here was a woman not only without fear, but apparently without cause of it.

'Can I help you?' she asked.

'I hope you can,' Whittaker said. 'Is Mrs. Gann here?'

'Eve?' the woman said, as if startled. 'She's not here right now, but I'm expecting her. Won't you come in?'

'Thank you,' Whittaker said; 'I'll be glad to.'

Eve.

It was a fact that Bob Gann had never talked of her as Eve; often of his wife, of 'her' and 'she', but never simply Eve. Whittaker found the two names running through his mind: Eve Gann.

He walked in, and the door closed firmly.

'When do you expect her?' he asked.

'I thought maybe you were Eve,' the sister said, and looked up at him thoughtfully. Something in her expression told Whittaker that she recognised him; a swift spasm of what might well be alarm showed in eyes which were grey but not dawn-grey like . . . Eve's.

She led the way into a large living-room, which was as cool as a room could be. The curtains were drawn. Colours splashed the walls and the furniture, bright yet toning in. The room gave an impression both of comfort and modernity, it had a lived-in look. By the side of an armchair was a small table, with a glass half-filled with coca-cola, a glass ashtray, cigarettes, and a book of matches. On the chair itself a book was open, somewhere in the middle. Folded on another table close to hand was a newspaper, and looking up from the newspaper was a picture of—Whittaker himself.

His heart began to beat faster.

'Won't you sit down?' Eve's sister asked, and added: 'I ought to introduce myself. I'm Eve's sister, Rachel Defoe.'

There was the photograph; but he couldn't make up his mind, at once, what to call himself. Anything except Whittaker or White. She would guess that whatever name he gave was false, but no law compelled her to recognise a man from a photograph, and if he called himself Gibson, say, she would at least have an excuse for doing nothing about it, whereas if he called himself Whittaker . . .

'I'm a friend of Bob,' he said.

'I think I've heard of you,' Rachel Defoe said; she didn't exactly smile; just looked as if she would like to. 'Won't you have a drink?'

'A coke would be just fine.'

'Oh, have some beer,' she said. 'I always keep a can in the ice-box.'

'Thanks,' he said, 'I'll settle for beer.'

'Why don't you sit down?' she invited. 'I'll get it.'

She smiled this time, and went out of the room, across the small hall, into a room which he had just noticed. He had also noticed that there was a telephone in here; there might be in the other rooms, there was probably one in the bedroom of this apartment; it wasn't a cheap place. He watched the open door. He listened for furtive movements, the stealthy opening of a door, the lifting of a telephone, the sometimes almost inaudible ting! of sound as it was lifted. He heard nothing like that, and nothing furtive at all; there were sharper sounds, followed by her footsteps. Rachel Defoe brought in a glass and a can of beer— opened, so that he could pour it. She put this on a small table by the side of his chair, with a glass mat beneath it.

'Thank you.' He took out cigarettes.

'It was bad about Bob,' she said, very quietly.

'It was very bad.'

'Eve told me,' Rachel Defoe said, and hesitated, and then added more briskly, 'everything, I guess. We're sisters who get on well. Shall I tell you something?'

He waited.

'This will twist Eve right up,' she told him. 'It will be more than hell for her.'

'I think you're right.'

'I got that impression,' Whittaker said. 'Where is she, now?'

'She's been aboard the *Queen B.*, and with the police department part of the afternoon. I don't know where she is, right now. I hope she won't be long.' Rachel Defoe looked up at a small electric clock built into the wall, and at the same time stretched out for a cigarette. As she lit it, she gave Whittaker the impression that she was fighting her nerves, and he wondered if that were simply because he was here. She had seemed so free from fear.

'I'm beginning to get worried about Eve,' she said suddenly. 'She was to be back at nine o'clock.'

Now, it was half-past eleven.

Whittaker said slowly, worriedly, 'Wouldn't she call you if she expected to be late?'

'I'd certainly expect her to call me.'

'Can't you guess where she is?'

Rachel Defoe said: 'I can guess that she is out looking for the man who killed Bob—for the man who began all this. There's talk that Bob and that woman Gregson were killed by the same man, by the man Camponi who was found with a broken neck.' Her gaze was very straight. 'It's just talk,' Rachel went on. 'Even if he were the killer, Camponi was only a legman.'

'Could anyone be sure?'

'It's reasonable,' said Rachel Defoe, and glanced at the

clock again.

They sat in silence.

'If we knew where to start looking,' Whittaker said, 'we could start looking. You could also ask the police if they know where she is.'

'Eve wouldn't like that.'

'They've killed several times, and they could kill again.'

He shivered, inwardly.

The thought of Eve Gann dead was sufficient reason to cause that. He believed that he could see that the same kind of fear was in this woman, too. When he had come, there had been a kind of peace, but that had gone.

'I could call the police,' she said, 'but if I do that, then they'll know where to find'—she broke off for a long moment, and then added deliberately—'Eve.'

'Doesn't she want that?'

'She said she half expected a friend,' Rachel Defoe told him, and then added sharply: 'You know who she half expected. She wouldn't want anyone else to be here waiting for him.'

Whittaker sat in silence, which lasted for a minute or two, but which seemed to last for hours. Then he said mildly:

'Will you call the police about Eve, at once?'

He saw the woman's expression soften, knew that she would think along the same lines as Eve. Two sisters, worthy of being sisters, from magnificent stock. She actually smiled.

'I needn't tell them who it is calling,' she said slowly. 'I can just ask them to look for Eve. I wouldn't care so much if that man hadn't telephoned.'

Whittaker went very still.

'What man? And when?'

'I don't know who, and he called not long before you came.'

'What did he want?'

'He asked for Eve.' Rachel was sitting very straight in her chair and watching Whittaker intently. 'He just asked for her, and when I said she wasn't at home he hung up.'

'No name?'

'No.'

Whittaker said, 'What window overlooks the street, Mrs. Defoe?'

'This one,' she said. 'And I'm not married.' She got up and

went to the window, and he followed her quickly and stopped her from touching the curtains.

'Put out the main light, then keep to one side, please,' he said, and she obeyed. He stood flat against the wall on the other side of the window, and gradually pulled the curtains aside. There was just the faint light from the reading lamp by her chair. He could hear her breathing. He opened the curtains wide enough to look out, and was quite sure that he could not be seen.

He could see the sidewalk across the road, the trees in the riverside gardens, the parked cars. Two cars were moving slowly, their lights glowing. Another came from the opposite direction, its headlights on. From here, they didn't look very bright, but they cast shadows—of other cars, of lamp-posts, of trees and bushes.

They cast the shadow of a man who stood by a tree nearly opposite the apartment building.

Whittaker said briskly: 'I'm going downstairs. Watch from here, and if Eve comes before you see me down there, open the window and shout.'

'All—right,' Rachel Defoe said, 'I'll do that.'

Whittaker turned away. He didn't want to scare her too much, and yet he felt badly scared. The watching man was watching *here*. Coincidence just wouldn't stretch that far. The man had seen Whittaker enter, and if he were a friend of Ricky and Blick, he almost certainly knew what Whittaker looked like; yet he had allowed him to come.

What drew this Ricky towards the Ganns?

Whittaker didn't force the questions, but went out quietly, carefully, making sure that the flat wasn't watched from up here. He went down one flight of stairs, for the same reason, then called the elevator. It came purring up. In a few seconds, he was stepping into the hall. The light was bright, and the watching man couldn't fail to see him. He went out briskly, swinging his arms and bending his body, so that he wouldn't look tall. He crossed the road diagonally, away from the watcher, and was sure that Rachel could see him; so her swift fears should be quietened.

He walked a hundred yards along the street, towards the first corner, then turned into the silent gardens. There were tarred paths, there were the bushes and the trees, and there was grass; dried and yellow and crisp underfoot. More cars passed, but none of them with their headlights.

A cab turned the corner, a yellow beetle with its engine snarling. It slowed down. It stopped outside the apartment house, and someone got out. Whittaker could see above the roof of the cab; the passenger was a woman, and he felt quite sure that it was Eve.

He moved, very swiftly.

He reached the spot where the watcher had been as the driver started his engine and the car moved off. He saw the man, now away from the cover of the tree, and watching Eve. She walked into the building. The outer doors were open, and didn't swing to.

The watcher's right arm was raised.

'Want something?' whispered Whittaker.

The man swung round, smack into his clenched fist. The crack must have sounded as far as Eve, but she was through the inner doors, which were swinging to behind her. The man hit the ground with the kind of thump which Blick had made; everything in his body must have been mixed right up. His gun slithered along the ground and came to rest in the kerb; it didn't go off.

Whittaker picked it up, making two he'd got, both with silencers.

He picked the man up, too; one small, lean man, whose limbs and muscles were slack, and who still didn't know what had hit him. Whittaker hoisted him to his shoulder and carried him into the shadows of the trees. Except for distant traffic, it was very quiet. Lights shone from some of the windows, but none from the window of Rachel Defoe's apartment. There were street lamps, too, and across the Hudson the lights of New Jersey. A ship moved sluggishly downstream. A bunch of cars, ten or twelve of them, snorted along the parkway, as if they were in a desperate hurry to outpace each other; when they passed and it was quiet, Whittaker could see the lights on the George Washington Bridge, looking as if they were suspended high in the night sky.

He put the man down, flat on his back, and in the dim light here, saw him move. He waited two minutes, and then said:

'You're going to talk, and you're not going to waste time. Who sent you after Mrs. Gann?'

The man's breathing had the gustiness of a spring storm; he couldn't get the breath in or out quickly enough. He was quivering, too.

Whittaker gripped his right wrist; a man with powerful fingers can do a lot with a twist or two. He twisted. The man's whole body flinched, and the breathing grew louder, more gusty.

'*It was Ri* . . .' he began, and then added with a gasp, 'It was Ricky!' he breathed.

'Where can I find Ricky?'

The man babbled: 'Ricky's the boss! He sent me——'

'Where can I find him?' Whittaker's grip tightened savagely.

'I don't know, I . . . don't do that, you're breaking my arm! Don't do that!'

'*Where can I find Ricky?*'

The man was writhing.

'You know I can't tell you that! If I were to tell you, I guess—*don't do that!*'

'Just tell me where to find Ricky.'

'He'll kill me!' the man sobbed. 'He'll kill me! He's at the Waldorf, with a pal, he——'

'What pal?'

'He's with a guy named Pirran,' the man said, and the sobbing note was still in his voice. 'He's with Pirran at the Waldorf.'

Whittaker didn't speak, didn't move, except to relax his grip. This Ricky, and Pirran, were together at the Waldorf-Astoria. Pirran, who should have been dead, was alive. And Ricky . . .

Whittaker ought to have been ready, but wasn't.

The man kicked at him savagely; the toe of his shoe caught Whittaker under the jaw and rocked him backwards. While he was falling, the man leapt to his feet, turned and darted off, away from the apartment house and away from the danger.

CHAPTER XII

BRIEF SANCTUARY

'Do you know why they should want to kill you?' Whittaker asked.

He stood in front of Eve Gann.

In the kitchen, behind him, Rachel was moving about, making subdued sounds. Everything else was subdued when Whittaker was alone with Eve. He scanned her face—every feature; every line; the fine colouring of her lips, her skin, her hair, her eyes. He was aware of that oneness between them, yet at the same time it was edged with wariness—almost with suspicion. The question seemed to carry with it the seeds of disaster; implied that she did know why this Ricky should want to kill her. Beyond that was another question: that she might know why Bob had been killed, that none of this was as simple as it appeared to be.

Her gaze was as steady as his.

'No,' she said, 'I can't imagine.'

'First Bob, then you.'

'I know.' She didn't smile, but there was an easing of the darkness of her gaze. 'And you, in between.'

Whittaker relaxed.

'Yes,' he agreed, 'they tried to get me.'

He touched his swollen jaw, and winced, turned away from her, and was glad to sit down. If there was a thing he didn't like to admit, it was that he was tired.

He was, though, and knew that it wasn't all due to the heat.

'You should have something on your face,' Eve said. 'You'd better come with me. Rachel will be some while making those sandwiches.' She waited for him to get up. Getting up was an effort. He followed her into a bathroom which shimmered with sea-green tiles and chromium, and first bathed his chin where the man had kicked him, then put on a salve. It felt easier. He knew the contentment of being ministered to . . . by her.

They went back into the living-room, to find that Rachel had brought in ham-and-turkey sandwiches, blueberry pie, cheesecake and coffee. It was all set on a low round table in the living-room.

'Now come and get it,' she said.

She was as calm as Eve, and as calm as Whittaker, but it wasn't quite genuine; it was something imposed on a turmoil of uncertainty, and of fear. He had been wrong in thinking that Rachel knew no fear; it burned as deep in her as in her sister.

Eve was dressed as she had been when she had driven him from Scarsdale that morning, in a dark blue linen which sheathed her; the trimmings of white fell softly against her skin. She looked tired, also; as if her eyes would close the moment she eased off the pressure she was exerting on herself.

It was half an hour since the man had run away.

Whittaker said, 'Thanks very much,' and took a sandwich and started to eat as if he hadn't eaten for weeks. He felt a kind of lethargy, but knew that he had to fight it off—or someone would fight it off for him. 'Eve, there's one thing to remember.'

'What's that?'

'They've failed once with you, but they'll probably try again.'

'Yes,' she agreed.

'Is there a place where you could go, and where they couldn't find you?'

She paused.

'Is there?'

'There's a place where you could both go,' said Rachel quietly.

'No,' Eve answered quickly. 'You're too deeply involved already.'

'Don't you think I want to be?'

'That doesn't mean that you should be.'

'Don't be ridiculous, Eve,' Rachel said, with complete calmness. 'It's the only sensible thing for you and for Mr. Whittaker to do. I've some friends,' she went on, looking at Whittaker, 'in Harlem. That's about the last place that anyone will think of looking for Eve or for you. It isn't far away from here, and it's on the west side. You could drive or you could walk.'

'I've work to do,' Whittaker said, 'but I'd like to think that Eve was in a safe place.'

Neither of them spoke for a moment, but obviously he

96

had switched their thoughts from Eve to him. He finished the sandwich, and leaned forward for another.

'I want to see Pirran,' he went on. 'And I want to see a man named Ricky.'

He knew, as surely as if they had both cried out, that the name meant something to them, and that something wasn't good. He bit into the sandwich, pretending to notice nothing, for this was better unforced. For a few seconds, he wondered if they were going to explain why the name affected them so, but he did nothing to prompt them.

Rachel moved forward, to pour out coffee.

'What do you know of Ricky?' asked Eve quietly.

'He's been mentioned twice,' Whittaker said. 'The man who went to see if Olive Johns had the packet said that Ricky sent him. The man who shot at you said that Ricky sent him. I'd be interested to know who Ricky is.'

'Will you have some more coffee?' Rachel asked.

'Thanks.'

'And another sandwich?'

'No, thanks.'

'Ricky,' said Eve, slowly, and left the name hovering in the air for what seemed a long time; 'I can tell you who Ricky is. He's Nelsom Rickett. He owns the Owl Club, the Green Club, the Red Spider Club. He owns a dozen—or it may be a hundred—strip-joints and night-spots in New York and Jersey City; he owns more upstate, New York, he owns more in Atlanta and more in Florida, and he owns some in Chicago and some of the big cities in the Middle West. Bob'—she brought her husband's name out without effort and without a change of tone—'always said that he would die happy if he could break Ricky.'

There was silence.

'Is he that bad?' asked Whittaker heavily.

'He's just—bad.'

'Where can I find him?'

'You're not going to look for him,' said Eve firmly. 'Not tired and all washed up like you are now. That would be crazy. You need a good night's sleep before you go anywhere else, and that's what you're going to have.' She said that mechanically, and then added almost under her breath, 'So it's Ricky.'

'That's what they say.'

All this time Rachel had been sitting there, listening, pouring coffee, eating. She cut the cheese-cake and put a generous slice on Whittaker's plate. Then, looking from her sister to Whittaker, she said:

'Eve's right, Mr. Whittaker. You must have a long sleep.'

He could argue, and it wouldn't make any difference. They could talk from now until they fell asleep in their chairs, and they wouldn't stop him from trying to see Ricky and Pirran tonight, but they needn't know that. Tired though he was, a dozen different questions thrust themselves into his mind, and none was easy to answer.

'Have it your own way,' he said. The cheese-cake was delicious, and actually drew his thoughts. It had a dreamlike creamy flavour.

'I can drive you,' Rachel volunteered quickly.

'We can get a cab,' Eve said.

'Where's your car?' Whittaker asked.

'It's down town.'

He didn't ask why.

'We can walk. We don't want to be seen by——'

'I don't know why you're wasting time,' Rachel said. 'I'm going to drive you.' She smiled. 'Joanna wouldn't let you in unless I were there to vouch for you; she would think you were going to start living in sin! Will you have more cheese-cake, Mr. Whittaker?'

'Well, thanks.'

Eve said: 'Rachel makes the best cheese-cake in New York. You're a good judge.'

'I can believe it,' he said.

Ten minutes later they were sitting in Rachel's car, which was parked nearby; there was comfortable room for all three on the front seat. As far as Whittaker could see, no one watched; and no one seemed to follow.

Whittaker made as sure as he could of that as Rachel drove off. She took the first opportunity for a U-turn, and then drove swiftly. It was after midnight, but there was still a lot of traffic about, especially on the parkway. She didn't turn off for some time, and when she did it was into 130th Street. From then, Whittaker lost himself. They drove along streets which were brightly lit, past shops which screamed the usual slogans, past open restaurants and shadowy cafés. It might have been any busy section of New York, except for one thing which he soon noticed. He was an old friend of New York, he liked to think he knew it well, but he would never stop being surprised, almost startled and certainly fascinated when he drove here.

Everyone he saw was coloured; it was as if he had been driven out of the white man's civilisation that he knew, into one which had the same surface look, the same kind of buildings, lights, colours, bustle, vitality—but in a different country where white men were not known. He looked right and left as Rachel drove obviously with thorough knowledge of the streets, and was almost sorry when she turned into a darker street than most, and slowed down. Against the pale night sky, lit by the reflection of a million neon lights, he saw a tower with a lighted cross on top; and steps and a notice-board, an illuminated sign saying: *First Church of the Gospel Truth.*

'Wait here,' Rachel said, 'I'll see Joanna.'

She got out and closed the door.

Eve eased herself away from Whittaker, and stretched out for a cigarette, which stood in a small container fastened to the dashboard. If she felt the tension that he did, she hid it; but her calm was unnatural, and forced. The cigarette glowed. Whittaker was watching in the mirror. No car turned after them and he felt sure that no one had followed.

Could he *be* sure?

'Rachel's full of good works,' Eve said suddenly.

'I can believe that, too.'

'I don't think anyone has more friends,' Eve went on, 'especially in Harlem. They love her, here.'

He said, 'She's good to know.'

Eve was better to know. She could sit here as calmly as this, hiding her fear. Of course, the full impact of grief had not hit her yet, it might not, until she had finished her search for Bob's killer.

She lit the cigarette. Two men passed, glancing into the car; both were coloured men. Whittaker's muscles grew taut. They sauntered by. On the other side of the street a couple stood in a doorway, not watching the car, not interested in anything but each other.

'They don't get a lot of help,' Eve went on. 'Rachel does all she can to bridge a gap she says should never exist.

Sometimes I agree with her, and sometimes I don't.' Her profile, lit up by the red glow of the cigarette, was quite beautiful. 'Sister Joanna is the Minister of the church, and at the back there's a kind of hostel, with rooms or cubicles for any who need them—and a lot of Harlem people need them.'

Whittaker didn't speak.

Eve said in a quicker voice: 'Here she comes. Mr. Whittaker, I don't want you to go out again tonight. I'm shaken deep down now that I know Ricky is involved. It doesn't make any difference in the long run, but——'

'All right,' he said. 'Don't worry.'

His hand closed over hers, in a kind of promise which he didn't intend to keep. The night was too precious. Tomorrow he might not know where to find Pirran. He wasn't sure that Ricky was of first importance, he was quite sure about Pirran. He knew what he wanted to do with the little fish-like man.

'It isn't often white people stay here by night,' said Eve. 'Even Rachel may find it hard to persuade Joanna that you should.'

There was movement along the alley which led from the side of the church. Rachel came, followed by a shorter woman, plump, dressed in a dark robe which almost touched the ground, her hands held in front of her, almost as a nun might be. In the light from the illuminated signs, she was smiling gravely. Whittaker opened the door and got out.

'Rachel said, 'This is Sister Joanna, Mr. Gibson, and she will be happy to give you both hospitality for the night.'

'It will be my very great pleasure, sir,' said the woman, in a deep, soft voice. 'My guest room is at your disposal.' Her English was as good as if she had been educated at one of the universities, and she had a fascinating voice. Now, Whittaker saw her crinkly hair was braided and coiled, like Eve's, and that some kind of semi-precious stones sparkled in it. 'And also you, Mrs. Gann; I'm very pleased to see you again.' She shook hands with each of them. 'You are sure you cannot stay, Miss Rachel?'

'I don't think I should,' Rachel Defoe said briskly. 'I'll leave them to you, Sister.'

She got into the car and drove off.

Sister Joanna led Whittaker and Eve along a narrow alley,

down a flight of stone steps, and then into a door of a building at the back of the church. They entered a wooden hallway. A door stood open, and inside were a dozen camp-beds, with a man on each; most of the men were asleep, some looked with tired, dark eyes towards the trio as they passed.

At the end of the passage was another, leading to an apartment with several rooms. Gravely, pleasantly, Sister Joanna showed them their rooms, each tiny but sufficient; the living-room; the bathroom. Then she left them, as if she knew that she had done everything she could.

Eve said quietly, 'Neil, you haven't promised me that you won't go out.'

He didn't speak. He thought, 'Neil.' He made himself smile.

'Haven't I?' he said.

CHAPTER XIII

NIGHT

EVE stood very close to Whittaker, at that moment. It was easy to forget that the chief reason for the shadows in her eyes was the death of her husband. It was easy to forget that tragedy had brought them together. Here they were, man and woman, and the attraction between them was so strong, so clear, that each sensed it, and each knew that the other did, too.

Neither moved.

'You wouldn't understand,' she said; 'you don't belong here and you can't tune yourself in. Nelsom Rickett is—very powerful. Corrupt and merciless, too. Bob swore that he would get him, and now I think it's obvious that he was much nearer than he thought. Knowing that Ricky is behind this makes all the difference. It isn't a thing we can do in a few hours, or in a few days. It will be a long, long time.'

'First,' Whittaker said, 'we have to make sure that Ricky is behind it.'

Now her eyes flared with unexpected fire.

'Both men said so! You——'

'Eve,' he said, 'I've worked in New York before. I know perhaps more than you think. Certainly I know that there are Bob Ganns by the dozen in the police force, sometimes powerless because of the Nelsom Ricketts. The police hate the Ricketts, but they aren't alone. Others hate them, too. The question I'm asking myself is simple: why did two men *name* Ricky? If he's so powerful, would legmen like these two even know who they work for? And if they knew, would they talk?'

The flame died.

'I see what you mean,' Eve said, and turned away, and added in a low-pitched voice. 'You could be right.'

'For my money, Pirran could be the key to all of this,' went on Whittaker. 'He's the man I want to talk to first, who might know all the truth, especially the truth about the contents of that packet, I'm told he's at the Waldorf-Astoria, with Ricky. Does Ricky live there?'

'I've never heard it said that he does.'

'We can make sure that Pirran is staying there,' said Whittaker. 'Or you can. You must know friends of Bob——'

'I can find out where Pirran is,' Eve agreed, and moved towards him. She took his hands; hers were surprisingly cool. 'Neil, don't go out tonight. Have some rest. You're not fit to go out and risk more fighting, more running, more gunning. You had no rest last night. You've been on the run all day; you'll burn yourself out.' The grip of her fingers was very tight, and there was anguish in her voice. 'You'll burn yourself right out, and you mustn't do it, not in a fight like this. Don't go!'

He understood, somehow, that she wasn't only talking to him. She was talking to a ghost. She was saying to him what she had said a hundred—perhaps a thousand—times to Bob Gann. She had always been ignored; he could tell that from the hopeless look in her eyes. She believed that she was fighting a losing battle, as she had often done in the past.

He said: 'It's nearly two o'clock. I'll sleep until five.' He grinned at her. 'If I oversleep, that'll be my trouble! You find out if Pirran has a room at the Waldorf-Astoria, and then go to bed yourself. You're not looking at your freshest; it's been quite a day for you.'

'Yes,' she said quietly, 'it's been quite a day. Take your

clothes off, mind, and get into bed: don't just doze.'

She was probably sure that if he did that, he would not wake at five o'clock.

'I'll be in bed when you come back with the message about Pirran,' he promised.

He was.

'Yes,' Eve told him. 'He's there, in Suite 914.'

'Suite 914,' echoed Whittaker, and as he did so he remembered the stateroom on the *Queen B.*, which he had left an age ago. *A14* there; 914 here. Odd thing, coincidence, and you met it all over the world. Coincidence didn't make sense; but then, little did. What sense did he make, lying here, watching Eve as she went out, seeing her face turned towards him as she closed the door, wishing, against all the beliefs he held, that she wasn't going.

Wishing. . . .

Five minutes later he went out to make sure that her door was locked. It was.

*   *   *

It was five minutes past five.

Whittaker woke on the instant. It was very dark. He listened for any sounds which might have disturbed him, but there was none. Then he remembered. He got out of bed slowly, found his lighter, flicked it and then found the light switch. He dressed without any kind of haste. He knew that he needed ten minutes to wake up properly; in those ten minutes he would be as good as new—except for his jaw. That was stiff. A man who had named Ricky had kicked him, a kick which wouldn't be forgotten for a long time.

He wished he had a hot drink of tea or coffee.

He lit a cigarette, although it made his parched mouth seem even drier, and went to the door. He opened it cautiously. There was no light on, except the one behind him, casting his shadow. Eve's door was still closed. He tried the handle, for reassurance; the door was locked, of course.

He crept to the front door. As he neared it, he heard a strange harsh sound, and realised that a dozen men were snoring. Some loud, some harshly, some on a low-pitched note—there was the night's song of the down-and-outs who had come to Sister Joanna's sactuary.

He grinned.

A light was on in the big dormitory, and the door was open. No one looked towards him as he passed.

Outside it was cool, now.

He went swiftly, making little sound along the alley towards the street; then, right, without knowing where he was heading. He reached a corner, read a sign and felt at home: this was Park Avenue. Most of the shops were brightly lit, but there were few cars about, except those parked in the side street and on Lennox itself. A café was open, and he saw two coloured men sitting on stools, a coloured man in a white chef's hat serving them. If he went in there, he would be too noticeable; so far, he'd got away with it, and felt sure that he hadn't been followed to Sister Joanna's; he mustn't add to risks.

He walked past the restaurant.

Two coloured policemen were standing together at a corner, watching him with the wary curiosity of the police everywhere.

They would be more suspicious of a white man alone, here, at this hour. He could see their guns. He felt the temptation to hurry, but didn't let himself. Shoulders hunched, he slouched past.

They didn't follow.

He wondered if he would have luck with a taxi, when he saw four at a stand. The driver of the first was too eager to have a customer to worry about looking hard at him.

'Where for, suh?'

'Park and 48th,' Whittaker said.

'Sure thing.'

So the City did sleep. Or, at least, it lived sluggishly in these early hours. Here and there a moving car, here and there an open restaurant. There were lights everywhere, lights of every colour and of brilliance, flashing lights, moving lights, dazzling lights, all fighting the dawn, which was coming fast. It was like a garish city of uneasy sleep— but as he drew nearer the heart, there were more cars, more people, more open doorways, more policemen. The cabby took him down Broadway for a while, and then switched off. The mass of lights near Times Square looked fantastic in their dazzling brilliance.

'Park and 48th, suh.'

'Fine!' said Whittaker. 'Thanks.'

Two people, a broad man and a silver-haired girl, came out of the big hotel as he approached it. A patrol car crawled by. A commissionaire stood staring into the lights of the wide avenue. The windows outside the hotel were brightly lit, the models in them appealing to the night itself. Whittaker felt absolutely secure in his anonymity; only people who had seen him would have any real chance to recognise him; the other risk was negligible. Yet he was on edge every moment. He felt his automatic, and the gun which he had taken from the man outside Rachel's apartment. One too many? Not in a thousand years. He went briskly into the hotel, and the commissionaire took no notice of him at all. The revolving doors squealed. Inside, it was almost empty and very bright. Three clerks stood waiting for customers who didn't come. He ignored them and went to the bellboy's desk. The 'boy' greeted him smartly.

'You know Mr. Pirran's room?'

'Yes, sir!'

'Is Mr. Rickett still up there?'

'No, sir, Mr. Rickett left two to three hours ago.'

'That's too bad,' Whittaker said. He went towards the elevators, and there, standing with hollow-eyed hopefulness, was another 'boy'. 'Ninth, please.'

'Yes, sir.'

Nine floors—four seconds.

Whittaker stepped out into the luxuriously carpeted passage, and saw something which he'd forgotten and which nearly beat him. The floor clerk. It was a woman, perky and bright in spite of her black dress, who look at him curiously. She had a pencil in hand and lists on the desk in front of her.

She also had a newspaper, open, with a photograph face upwards. *His* photograph.

'Good evening, sir.' She smiled.

'Evening,' said Whittaker. 'Mr. Pirran?'

'Are you expected, sir?'

'Just tell him,' Whittaker said. 'It's a message from Mr. Rickett. I'll be at his door. Which way is it?'

She seemed to hesitate. If she glanced down at the picture, would she recognise him? It was one taken on board the *Queen B.*, enlarged, good in its way. He was grinning broadly, though, and looked years younger than he was.

Suddenly she said, 'To your right, sir, and then right again.'

His openness had fooled her, as it had fooled the others. But his certainty had been swallowed up in harsh doubts. He went to the nearest corner and turned it, then waited. He didn't hear her on the telephone, didn't hear her get up. Yes, he'd fooled her. He followed the directions, now, and saw the light over the door of 914. He waited outside it, listening. He could only guess what Pirran would do when he was disturbed by the telephone; he couldn't guess how long it would be before the door opened. He waited for what seemed a long time. His ears were cocked, to pick up the slightest sound of anyone approaching from either direction. No one did. Then he heard a sound inside the suite, and he stepped very close to the door, with his left foot ready to move forward so that the door couldn't be closed.

There were sounds as of a chain being moved; then the key turned in the lock. Next the door began to open, and he judged that it wouldn't open far if the man there had his way.

He saw part of a face through the narrow gap.

'Who——'

Whittaker put his shoulder to the door and it flew open. The man staggered back, off his balance. Whittaker slipped in, closed the door and locked it, slid the key into his pocket, and then went for the man.

It was the one who had been there to shoot Eve, who had kicked him in the jaw. He hadn't recovered his balance and was still stumbling, but his right hand was groping for his pocket. Whittaker followed up, and the man folded, easily and neatly. He dropped on to the floor, still clutching the gun, and Whittaker took it from him and smiled tautly at the open door of the bedroom.

Pirran gaped at him.

'Hullo, Gus,' said Whittaker, and waved the gun he had just taken. One too many! He raked the outer room with his gaze, made sure that no one else was there and pushed Pirran into the bedroom. Pirran didn't seem able to move or to speak; he just went back obediently like clockwork. He looked more like a dead fish than ever, and his neck veins worked like agitated gills.

No one else was in the bedroom, which was probably a disappointment for Pirran. There were two beds, one of them rumpled. A bathroom led off it, and with a hand at the back of Pirran's neck Whittaker looked in this bathroom. That was also empty. He went back into the sitting-room, thrusting Pirran before him: the little man hadn't yet started to make any sound. The gunman lay as if sleeping. Whittaker took off the man's coat, then put it on him again, back to front, and buttoned it up. Then he used the man's own tie to fasten his ankles together.

Pirran gaped.

'Lead the way back to the bathroom,' Whittaker ordered.

Pirran gulped and obeyed.

'What——?'

Whittaker took his right arm, twisted, then lifted and carried him. He lowered him into the bath, then ripped a linen towel into strips, tied Pirran's wrists behind him, and next hooked the bound wrists over the big tap. It wasn't exactly comfortable, but it would do him no harm.

Pirran seemed to be suffering so much from shock that he couldn't speak. He had hardly any hair, his eyelashes were so fair that they were barely defined against his pale face. His eyebrows were almost colourless, too; an odd-looking man made odder now by what seemed an all-consuming fear.

But he managed to find words at last.

'Yo—yo—you're Whittaker!'

'That's right,' said Whittaker. 'I work for you, remember? How would you like to drown?'

Pirran echoed, '*Drown?*'

'That's right. All I have to do is turn on the tap, and hold you down. It wouldn't take long, but it wouldn't be nice.'

'You—you daren't . . .!'

Whittaker said savagely: 'I'd dare, and I'd like it! You double-crossing little swine.'

He broke off.

Pirran was sweating.

Whittaker rasped: 'Who did you do a deal with? Maisie?'

There was a long pause, as if Pirran were trying to make up his mind what to say. His lips worked. A little more pressure and he would crack wide open, but that would take time, and Whittaker hadn't much time to spare here.

As it was, he should soon be on his way.

Pirran said huskily:

'Sure, sure, I did a deal with Maisie. It was soon after she came aboard. She told me she was working with Camponi, but didn't like the guy. She said I could rely on her and Olive—Olive Johns. I paid her a thousand pounds to leave me alone, Whittaker, so that I could—could live without fear. Any man's got a right to live without——'

Whittaker broke in, 'And Camponi found out?'

'Yes, he—made Maisie talk. They drugged me and he took the packet . . . but you *know* what happened!'

'Camponi killed Bob Gann and Maisie, yes,' Whittaker said. 'I can even understand him killing Maisie if she double-crossed him. But why kill Bob? And why try to kill me?'

'I don't know,' Pirran said wheezily. 'God's truth, I don't know!'

'You know he got hold of a dummy packet, not the real one?'

'That—that's what Ricky said. I didn't know until tonight.'

Whittaker leaned forward very lowly. He could read Pirran's tension and his fear; time pressed very hard, but minutes spent now might save hours later.

'So you didn't,' he said roughly. 'Listen, Pirran, you were left alive, remember? Camponi seemed to run amok because of what you *might* have told me and Bob. That's what he said to Olive. He knew you had certain information. He was afraid you'd told Bob Gann and me; so, he killed Bob. So —what did you know that mattered so much?'

'It can't be true!' Pirran gasped. 'He couldn't have said——'

'It can be true,' Whittaker said. 'It could explain why you're alive, too. Know what I think, Pirran? I think you know something which is deadly to Ricky, and Camponi discovered that. So Camponi kept you alive, but killed anyone you might have talked to. Camponi's dead, but you're living on borrowed time. Ricky daren't kill you in case you've left that secret knowledge behind for the posterity. You could have left a sealed envelope at your bank, or somewhere safe, Pirran. What *do* you know?'

'I tell you I don't know a thing!' Pirran gasped.

Whittaker's voice roughened.

'Why does Ricky suddenly come to terms with you?'

'He—he thinks I know where the packet is,' Pirran said hoarsely; 'thinks I'm the only one who can tell him, but I *don't* know!'

Did he know?

Could he lie like that when he was so frightened?

Whittaker stood staring down at him. He looked as if he were choking, and would soon collapse; and as if he were frightened of death.

Was there time to work in? Dare he stay?

Whittaker turned away, looked into the other room and made sure that the man there was still helpless. Then he returned to Pirran. He stood over him while Pirran gasped for breath.

Then Whittaker touched a tap.

He didn't turn it, because he wanted Pirran to understand just what he could do; wanted the man to realise that his life was in a stranger's hands. There was so little time, and it was possible that Pirran could tell everything that mattered in a few minutes. That was if Pirran could be put in the right frame of mind.

He had to be.

If he could withstand the strain of this and still be well enough to deceive Whittaker, he almost deserved to get away with it.

Almost.

'What—what are you doing?' he asked in a choky voice. 'What——'

Then he broke off, for Whittaker turned the water on.

CHAPTER XIV

JUST A LITTLE RIDE

PIRRAN made a whistling sound as the cold water ran on to his back, and began to shiver, to try to stand up. He couldn't. He looked piteously at Whittaker, who stood unmoving. The water ran, splashing now, and Pirran couldn't stop shivering.

'Where's the packet?' Whittaker asked flatly.

'I tell you I don't know! One was stolen from me, Ricky says it was a dummy. I don't know where the real one is.'

'What's in the real one?'

Pirran's teeth sounded like castanets.

'D-diamonds,' he stammered. 'A fortune in ice, a million dollars' worth. They're dynamite, Whittaker, and someone has them, but I don't know who.'

*   *   *

Whittaker couldn't be sure, but he thought that Pirran probably meant what he said. The man was too cowed to lie; cowed, cold, craven. And if that packet contained a fortune in diamonds, it would well explain violence and sudden deaths: that could answer many questions.

It was enough to make Ricky hold his hand, too; if he thought that Pirran had hidden the packet away he would try to do a deal.

Whittaker said, 'I'll untie you; you can give yourself a rub down.'

He stopped the water, helped Pirran out and flung him a towel. The man's ribs showed above his little pot-belly.

'Keep talking,' Whittaker went on. 'Where's Ricky now?'

'He left here a couple of hours ago,' Pirran said. He rubbed vigorously, but his teeth were still chattering. 'He said he'd give me a day to think it over. He—he left Moyan to watch me.'

'Is Moyan the man outside?'

'Yes, yes. He—he's dangerous, he——'

'Not for a little while,' said Whittaker brusquely. 'Where can I find Ricky?'

Pirran stopped towelling. With a towel draped round his skinny body, he took on a queer kind of dignity.

'Whittaker,' he said, 'Ricky is after those diamonds. He doesn't know where they are. He's mad. He's a killer. Don't cross Ricky. Don't go and see him. Sure, he killed Bob Gann, or Camponi did, and Camponi worked for Ricky, but don't take this fight to Ricky yet. Look for the diamonds. If you find them, then you can fight it out with Ricky. Then you'll have something to fight with.'

There seemed a lot of sense in that, and Pirran meant it;

110

that dignity sat well upon him.

Whittaker said: 'We'll see. Hurry up. We're going for a little ride.'

'What—what do you mean?' Pirran's dignity melted as fear came back. 'Where?'

'You'll see.'

'Ricky——'

'Ricky will come after us both, won't he?' Whittaker said roughly. 'You're the juiciest bait. Don't play your hand wrong, Pirran, you're still alive.'

Pirran muttered, 'Okay, I'll get dressed.'

Whittaker followed him into the bedroom. He didn't hurry, but neither did he dawdle. The other man was conscious and mad and scared: probably he was more scared of what Ricky might do, than of Whittaker.

Soon, Pirran was ready.

Whittaker said roughly, 'Don't forget, you'll live while you play the game my way.'

Pirran didn't speak.

He kept moistening his lips. Whether he had told the truth or not, it was obvious that he was scared. Did he expect anyone else here? Had Ricky a man outside in the passage? Or was Ricky or one of his men expected now? The certain thing was that they couldn't stay here. He had stayed too long already. He could try a downtown hotel, but that wasn't what he wanted.

At heart he knew where to go for a start.

Rachel Defoe's apartment would be safe enough, and Eve wasn't there. The risk was obvious: that Ricky was having it watched. Well, he could deal with Ricky's men. If he could get near the apartment and check it for a watcher, that would do. He could deal with any man, then get Pirran inside.

'Have you a car near here?' Whittaker asked abruptly.

'Wha—what's that?'

'Have you a car?'

'Sure, I——'

'What's the number?'

'New York, NYS741,' Pirran said hurriedly. 'It's a brown Chrysler, parked in 48th Street, near Park. Wh—wh—why?'

'I'd like to borrow it,' Whittaker said. 'Mind if I take your keys?' He waited until Pirran handed the keys over. He didn't pull a gun or attempt to pull a fast one; he seemed completely subdued; beaten.

'Which is the ignition?' Whittaker asked.

'The shiny one.'

'Okay—let's go!' Whittaker said. He put a hand on Pirran's shoulder and moved across the bedroom. When they reached the door, he said very quietly: 'You can call for help. You can run. You can kick me in the shins. Try any one of them if you want me to break your neck.'

Pirran said flatly, 'You wouldn't do it.'

'You don't have to believe me,' Whittaker said. 'Just put it to the test.' He put a hand on the door. 'We're going out. We're going to walk to the elevators, and you're going to keep one step ahead of me: no more. You're going to smile at the floor clerk and at the elevator boy, and at anyone who gets in our way. It's going to look as if we're buddies. Understand?'

'I—I'll do it,' Pirran said.

Whittaker opened the door a fraction. No one was in the passage so far as he could see. He opened the door wider, then let Pirran go out ahead of him. Pirran turned towards the elevators. Everything went according to plan; the floor clerk, the elevator, the great hall, the revolving-doors and the street.

It was full daylight now, and the morning dimmed the radiance of the window signs and the street lamps, but they were still on. Several cars passed, several people were on the move, on foot.

Whittaker turned towards 48th Street, repeating the number which Pirran had given him. He was weighing up the risks of going to Rachel's flat, and when he'd done it, knew that he had no choice; he had to start somewhere. Put Pirran to sleep, make sure that the apartment wasn't watched, take Pirran inside.

Rachel would play it his way, if he judged her rightly.

He reached the corner of 48th Street, with Pirran by his side: a subdued, scared little man—whose acquiescence was almost suspicious in itself.

Would he make a break and run?

Whittaker tried to cover everything. He saw no one watching and kept his fingers crossed.

Then he heard footsteps behind him—quick, and drawing closer.

Now, he *was* being followed; by a woman, not by a man.

He turned into 48th Street and saw a shiny brown Chrysler parked about five cars down. Pirran's. He crossed to it, with Pirran keeping a step ahead.

Whittaker reached the car and looked round.

Eve was coming.

Another car turned into the street and, as if it were a signal Pirran darted forward.

CHAPTER XV

PRISONER

THE car was coming swiftly, and Pirran was right in front of it as he ran. Whittaker shot out a foot. Pirran kicked against it and went sprawling. The driver of the car looked like a mask for Hallowe'en, mouth parted, teeth showing, eyes wide and bright with fright. His brakes squealed, the car skidded. Pirran, lying full length on the roadway, hadn't a chance—if the car came on.

It stopped, shuddering and screeching.

Whittaker grabbed Pirran, dragged him up and held him tightly. Pirran was gasping for breath. The driver, more relaxed now, was sitting at the wheel, hat at the back of his head, one hand at his wet forehead.

'Someone want to die?' he asked weakly.

'That was wonderful,' Whittaker breathed. 'I haven't seen driving like it in my life. That was simply *won*derful!'

'I'll say it was!' Eve was by his side, and her voice throbbed. 'I hope you're all right,' she went on, and ignored Whittaker as she looked at the driver. He was young enough to be impressionable. Whittaker forced a smile, waved inanely and, with Pirran still held tightly, he went to the brown Chrysler. Eve could handle this situation better than he. Eve was—well, Eve. He opened the rear door and let Pirran get in. Pirran had grazed his nose, and a little spot

113

of blood had welled up on it; and there was also a nasty graze on his cheek.

He was shivering.

'Good-bye, now,' Eve said, and waved as the driver moved off. He was looking round at her, and nearly ran into the line of parked cars.

She reached Whittaker.

'If I have to have a woman with me,' said Whittaker, 'let it be you.' He gave that time to sink in before he went on: 'I want a quiet place where we can talk to Pirran, and I wouldn't mind giving him a ride in the boot until he's in a talkative mood. Or a truthful one, he talks all right.'

Eve said, 'Boat?'

'The language difficulty will give me away before I'm finished,' Whittaker said ruefully. 'I never remember. Boot is English for trunk.'

'I think I know the place to go where we can hide him,' Eve said. 'I'll direct you. Shall I get in the back with him?'

'Yes, please.'

She got in. Whittaker closed the door, and then slid into his seat in front of the wheel. Before he started off, he handed her a gun; one of those he had 'won', with a silencer. She hesitated, then put in into her handbag, without a word.

There were things Whittaker had to remember. He hadn't driven a car with a left-hand drive for some time and hadn't had to keep to the right for a long time, either; he mustn't take any chances, and he had to re-orientate himself before he moved off. Eve still didn't speak. Pirran was breathing heavily, and kept making sounds which suggested that he would like to speak but hadn't the courage.

Eve said, 'Drive straight through to Tenth Avenue and turn right.'

'Thanks.'

He had some luck; there was ample room to get out of the parking space, so he didn't have much trouble. The unfamiliar gears handled easily, but when he put his foot on the accelerator he nearly stalled the engine. 'Easy,' he rebuked himself. He tried again, and the car slid forward; it hardly needed driving. The lights were with him. There was little traffic, although on Fifth Avenue and then on Broadway, little bunches were waiting at the lights, engines growling. He beat the Broadway lights; soon, he turned right on to Tenth Avenue. From the luxury of Park and Fifth, the aloofness of Madison and the bustle of Sixth Avenue, this was another world; as different as the *Church of the Gospel Truth* was from the apartments on Riverside Drive.

No one followed them as far as he could judge.

'Take the third block on the left,' said Eve.

'Thanks.'

'Slow down for a drive-in, when I tell you.'

He nodded.

They were among old buildings, high walls, garages, small factories. He saw the masts of ocean-going liners just beyond the end of the street and knew that he wasn't far from the Cunard docks. He fancied that he saw the bows of the *Queen B.* showing just above the roofs when Eve said:

'There's the drive-in, on your right.'

He took it.

They were in a yard, with a few wrecked automobiles standing about, much more wreckage piled up in a corner. The blank walls of a warehouse loomed up on two sides; on the fourth was the blank wall of a house.

'We won't be seen,' she said. 'What do you want to do?'

'Listen, Whittaker,' Pirran blurted out, 'I've told you the truth; it won't do any good to . . .'

Whittaker turned round in his seat, marvelling because there was room for him to move so freely in a car. He looked coldly at Pirran, whose colourless eyes were watering and who hadn't much courage left. Eve was sitting away from the man, but not looking at him; she gave the impression that she was completely indifferent to anything that happened to Augustus Pirran.

'Gus,' Whittaker said, 'it's daylight. I have to go under cover. So have you. Later, we'll have another little talk. If it doesn't work out the way I want it to, the police will be investigating a further case of homicide.'

The words came out flatly; he hoped that Pirran believed him, and he believed that Pirran would.

Pirran gasped: 'Who are you? Who do you really work for?'

'You were employing me,' Whittaker said. 'Remember? Where is that packet?'

'*I don't know. Gann must have stolen it from me!*'

'Prove that!'

'Who else . . .?'

Whittaker said: 'A lot of other people could have stolen it. Where is it?' He repeated harshly. The effort to blame had angered him.

'I don't know—I just don't know!' Pirran gabbled. 'I can't tell you any more than the truth.' He turned to Eve, his skinny hands stretched out, and he touched her; she drew back, as if away from corruption, but she couldn't draw right out of his reach. 'You make him understand! I've told the truth, no man can do more than that.'

'The trouble is that I don't believe you,' Whittaker said. 'You'll learn, in time.'

He struck the little man on the nape of the neck with the side of his hand. The blow jerked Pirran's head backwards, then sent it lolling forward. Eve stopped him from falling on her. Whittaker got out of the car and went to the back, unlocked the door of the trunk. It swung up smoothly of its own accord. It was huge with enough room for two men as large as Pirran. There were a few oddments in it, including a length of rope; that was all. He went round to the side of the car and lifted Pirran out, carried him to the trunk and put him inside. He used a handkerchief to gag him, and the rope to bind him. He went back for two cushions and put these under the man's head.

Then he locked the trunk.

Eve was sitting next to the driver's seat.

'Would you like me to drive?' she asked.

'I'd rather drive myself,' he said, and she nodded. He started the engine and turned the car round. 'When I said that I ought to go into hiding, I meant just that,' he told her. 'Would you recommend The First Church, or Rachel's apartment, or where? I was going to try Rachel for a start, but I had the silly notion that you wouldn't be about for a while.'

'I didn't trust you to stay away from the Waldorf,' Eve said. 'I'll think about the best place to go. How long do you want to stay under cover?'

'Until dark.'

'And then?'

Whittaker said: 'There might be a hue-and-cry for Pirran. Your friend Ricky will want to get him back. I think

116

that Pirran's got the key to all this, although I haven't yet seen how or why. I don't think he's told the truth, and I imagine we can scare him enough to make him. So, with Pirran a prisoner, we have quite a situation. We have the police looking for me, Rickett looking for Pirran, and Pirran working himself up into a fine state of jitters as soon as he comes round. He isn't sure any more that I'm working for him alone. He thinks I might be working for Scotland Yard, and he's afraid that I might be working just for myself. It's that which makes him really scared that I might kill him. That's the kind of pressure that might make him crack, and that's why I'd like to be able to hold him safely. I'd also like time for Ricky to show his hand. It seems as if Rickett thought it worth having a man to watch over Pirran, and if that's true——'

Eve said: 'Neil, will you tell me what's in your mind, instead of talking this way? I was never interested in words for words' sake.'

The grin he gave came quickly and spontaneously.

'All right,' he said, 'but the preliminaries were necessary. I think that Pirran still has that packet, or at least knows where it is. I think he hi-jacked it. I think that Rickett needs it badly, and would like to keep Pirran alive until he's got it. Having possession of that packet, or knowing where it is, is Pirran's one trump card. I'm not saying all this is true— I'm just saying that's how it could be. There's another possibility: that Pirran found out something about Ricky and is putting the black on Ricky. That seems as good a bet as the other and squares with what Camponi told Olive Johns.'

Whittaker paused to glance at Eve, who was staring straight ahead of her. He didn't tell her what was in the packet, and she didn't ask. The years must have taught her to repress her curiosity.

'The best way to get results is to let them all wonder what I know,' Whittaker went on. 'If we can hold Pirran, we should have the others worried. And we can take it easy for a day— you were saying that I needed some rest!'

'Yes,' Eve said soberly, 'you need rest.' But she was smiling faintly. 'We can borrow Rachel's car: no one will be so interested in that as in mine,' she pointed out shrewdly. 'We can't use this one much longer, anyway; there will be a search for it. In Rachel's car we can just spend the day—

idling. How does that sound? Central Park, maybe, or Rockefeller Centre, or in an hotel. On your own you'd be noticed, but two of us together won't be. We need a quiet day. You need rest, and still more rest. Why, we could even drive out to Scarsdale! I could call a neighbour and make sure the police and newspaper men aren't there. If they're not we would be all right, and you could talk to Pirran there.'

Whittaker said slowly, 'It's an idea.'

'No one need know, and I think we could get in without being seen,' Eve said with quick enthusiasm. 'Let's drive to get Rachel's car, first, shall we? We can pull up alongside, I can raise the trunk, and it won't take long to move Pirran from one car to another.'

Whittaker nodded.

'Then I can tell Rachel what we're going to do,' Eve said. 'Or something of it.'

He nodded again. 'Fine.'

'Let's go,' Eve said.

As he drove out of the yard he glanced at her; and he marvelled. Bob Gann himself couldn't have been cooler. No one could. As he had already judged, she had one thing in mind: finding out who killed her husband. Nothing else mattered; and she didn't look right or left any more than she had to. She was as good as Gann would be, in a similar quest; no one could be better.

He wondered what was going on in her mind, beneath all the calmness: what storms were raging, what turmoil seething. Did she think much of Bob, or had the objective of her desire driven the picture of him away, or at least dimmed it? Did she think of Mimi? Or the young Bob whom he hadn't seen?

He turned into Tenth Avenue again, needing no telling how to reach Riverside Drive or the corner with 59th Street.

As he approached he looked about with quickening tension. He sensed that in Eve, too. He scanned the park and the trees, the seats where old people sat and a few nurse-maids watched their children or rocked prams.

He saw no one who seemed interested in the apartment house.

He studied the parked cars. There were not so many as

there had been by night, and no driver sat with feigned nonchalance, no passengers lounged in the back.

Why not?

If it had been worth watching for Eve last night, why not now? Did the broad daylight explain that?

'There's Rachel's car,' Eve said; 'the blue Mercury.'

Whittaker drew alongside the blue car. No one was about, but there was a possibility that they could be overlooked from the houses bordering the road. That was a grave danger, but he had to take the risk. Cool as a man or woman could be, Eve brought him a car rug, from the trunk of the Mercury, and he opened the back of the brown car, spread the rug over Pirran and lifted him bodily.

In sixty seconds Pirran had changed resting places.

'You sit in the Mercury,' Eve said; 'I'll drive the Chrysler and park it a few blocks up. Just wait here. If anything makes you get away I'll be at Scarsdale tonight, after dark.'

'Don't be long,' Whittaker said.

She smiled, took the wheel of the borrowed car and moved off. He watched her until she was out of sight. No one followed her. He felt quite sure that she would be back before long. He could breathe freely for a while—a little while.

Even the thought made him feel guilty, careless and insecure.

He wondered whether the man had been found in the bath; whether anyone yet suspected that Pirran had been kidnapped. He kept trying to make sense of the different things that Pirran had told him. He came back, time after time, to some simple facts. That Gann had been killed; he, Whittaker, and Eve nearly been killed. There was Pirran's story of a vast wealth of diamonds; there was Camponi's story, to Olive Johns, of killing Bob and trying to kill him because of what Pirran might have told them.

That was on Whittaker's mind all the time. What could it be? And had Pirran lied? Did he know some secret deadly to Ricky?

If Pirran knew more than he had said, by nightfall he would be in a mood to talk. Hunger and fear did strange things to courage.

There was the day to spend.

With Eve Gann.

The thought of that brought a kind of peace. From the

119

time they had got into the brown Chrysler together, that peace had been upon them. When facts were facts, nothing could get in the way. There was the constant tension, the need for being on the look-out every moment, the continuing fear that they might be watched; that the police, on the one hand, or Ricky's men on the other, might pounce. Yet there was a kind of peace when they were together.

Eve had been gone ten minutes; not very long.

She'd been gone fifteen minutes.

She'd been gone for over twenty minutes, a hell of a time. He felt his heart pounding now; was much more afraid for her than for himself. He couldn't sit here and wait much longer. If Ricky had had a man watching, one who had seen her, snatched her, killed . . .

She was coming, walking calmly and superbly.

The sight of her calmed him; and the new peace told him how frightened he had been.

'I called Rachel,' she said; 'it's all right about the car.'

She got in beside him.

CHAPTER XVI

THE QUIET HOUSE

IT was dusk.

Here and there through the trees lights shone, yellow and inviting. There were no street lights in this part of Scarsdale. A car moved on a narrow road, not far off, swaying up and down, with the headlights making patterns upon the trees and the ground, now casting long shadows, now short ones; a silent, pirouetting ghost. It turned, at last, and the faint glow of its headlights vanished over a distant hill.

'Turn right along here,' Eve said, 'and you'll come to an empty plot.'

She had telephoned a neighbour, saying she wanted to collect something from home but wouldn't venture if newspapermen or the police were about. The neighbour had assured her that they had all gone; the last had left before dark. No one would expect Eve back here.

Whittaker turned right. He was not using headlights, and the sidelights gave hardly any glow at all. The road was uneven, but the car so sprung that it was easy to forget that. Soon, Eve told him where to turn in, and he put the nose of the car between trees and turned off the engine. The silence which followed seemed unbroken, but soon he became aware of noises nearby and noises afar off; the universe had no true silence.

Neither of them moved.

Whittaker thought, 'If I say anything about the day, there won't be a day to remember.'

He meant that it could be so easy to spoil. He meant that from now until the end of his life he wanted to remember this day.

After leaving Riverside Drive they had driven to Central Park, taking it easily, pulling up within sight of the big lake, and watching the children sail their model boats, pushing with sticks, urging with boisterous breath, or sitting back snugly and watching their engines taking the craft across with an even *chug-chug-chug*. Out of the park, and then a drive round the whole of Manhattan, fast as Whittaker wanted to drive, with a touch of exhilaration which speed and the might of the city gave him.

He had turned off the Roosevelt Drive near 106th Street and Eve had gone off, to buy sandwiches and pie, some chocolate, and some milk. They had sat overlooking the Bronx, to eat it. It had been a period of quiet in the middle of the storm, of relaxation in the middle of tension. Only now and again, when a policeman had appeared to look intently at him, had the tension grown taut.

He hadn't been stopped or questioned; his face might have been the face of a thousand men. He just wanted to remember the day without saying or doing a thing that would have given Eve cause for regret. She had none now. He believed that this day had helped her, and he would never quite know why.

Yet they sat still.

He stirred at last.

'Are you sure we won't be seen?'

'We can walk to the back of this plot,' Eve said; 'it hasn't been properly cleared. Then through the gardens of Elise

121

Gardner's home and across into mine. The only risk is bumping into someone.

No one seemed to be about.

Eve got out. They closed the doors of the car quietly, and Eve led the way at first. Soon he found her hand resting lightly on his arm, the guide and the touch that he needed. It was very dark. They rustled through long grass, and the twigs of a previous year cracked underfoot, but nothing else stirred. Here and there the lights; here and there the sounds of cars; that was all.

'Near here you'll find a creek,' she said; 'it's fenced both sides.'

'Crik?'

'Creek. Stream.'

'Ah!' They were whispering as if they were conspiring together. Whittaker walked with greater care, and made out the strands of wire, held up by posts several yards apart, and beyond it a narrow stream. The last of the afterglow shone on the surface, making it look like a narrow mirror in a dark room. The banks were steep and they could step across. He went first and turned to help Eve. She put both of her hands in his and he pulled her across, and for a split second of time they were close together. He released her, and they turned and walked as she directed, no longer arm-in-arm, until they came upon the darkness of her quiet house.

She was taking keys out of her handbag.

'Let's be sure it's as empty as it looks,' Whittaker warned. 'We'll walk right round.'

'If you like.'

There was no glimmer of light from any room, yet he was not wholly satisfied. It had been too quiet all day, too free from fear. That couldn't last.

The neighbours couldn't see in the dark; someone might have crept up here since darkness had fallen.

Whittaker heard and saw nothing.

'Have you a back-door key?' he whispered.

'Yes.'

'Let's go that way,' he said.

'All right.'

They still whispered.

The key made little sound, and the door did not squeak. With a quiet stealth they went from room to room, making sure that no one was there. It was quite empty. There was an atmosphere of the day's heat in the house, and Eve opened some windows to let in the coolness of the evening.

'Now I'm going back for Pirran,' Whittaker said.

'Shall I come with you?'

'No,' he decided. 'Stay on the back steps without a light. Have that automatic handy.'

She patted her handbag.

He went off, still uneasy, and filled with that sense of false security.

He knew that Eve doubted whether he would find his way back; there was so much that she didn't know about him. He went direct to the car as if he could see a trail, opened the back and lifted Pirran out. Pirran was conscious, and he wriggled a little, still mouthing something but making no sound that mattered.

They had taken the gag off, twice, to give him food and drink, and once Whittaker had walked with him for ten minutes. He walked now, limping badly.

Eve's figure, just a shadow, appeared from the back door.

'All right?'

'Yes.'

This time, when they went in, she locked the door and pulled the blinds, then switched on the kitchen light. Pirran blinked like an owl, and his mouth worked behind the gag. Whittaker untied the gag and saw the red marks on his lips, the ridges under his nose. He didn't feel at all sorry for Pirran, for a man who should have been dead but was alive. He could sense the change in the little man; the quivering of terror that was in him. He carried him into the living-room and dumped him in a chair and seemed to forget him.

Eve said, 'What will you do next?'

'When Pirran's told us all he knows,' said Whittaker, 'we can decide what it's best to do.'

'How will you know if he's telling the truth?'

Whittaker turned to look at Pirran.

'We'll know,' he said, and his gaze and his voice were as hard as the grip of his fingers could be. 'We'll know all right. Pirran has that packet. We'll get it. But Pirran can wait.' He stood up. 'We can't stir from the house tonight, Eve, so we aren't in any hurry.'

'Neil,' she said.

'Yes?'

'Don't throw time away. If Ricky comes after Pirran, then——'

'Rickett can't find us here,' Whittaker argued. 'No one followed us, no one knows where we are, no one saw us come here.' He sounded much more sure than he felt. 'It's a long way from the nearest house. Remember when the man came here and started shooting? No one heard a sound. No one will hear any noise that's made here. We needn't worry about Rickett catching up with us—unless we want him to.'

Eve didn't speak.

Whittaker said: 'I wouldn't object to overhearing Rickett and Pirran having a little chat, would you? We could fix it, if . . .' He stopped, and grinned and rubbed his great hands together. He seemed to be talking as if Pirran was a thousand miles away, not listening to them with his frightened eyes darting to and fro, and his parched tongue trying to moisten his dry lips. 'Rickett doesn't trust Pirran. If we were to let him know that Pirran had talked——'

Pirran squeaked, 'No, no, no!'

Whittaker turned to look at him.

There was a film of sweat on Pirran's wrinkled forehead, and on his lined upper lips. His mouth sagged and his chin drooped. His last vestige of courage seemed to have gone. There he was, like a damp expiring fish, and the only thing deep in him was fear. There were two fears; of what Whittaker might do to him and of what Rickett might do. The softening-up was as complete as it would ever be.

Whittaker said: 'I don't know how tough he is. I may have to ask you to go out of the room.'

'I don't understand,' Eve said, and didn't even smile.

She hadn't put a foot wrong, hadn't said a word out of place, from the moment of their meeting. She was a perfect foil, and Bob Gann must have found her so in his work as well as here at home. Bob Gann; the man who had died yesterday, which was a million years ago. Tall, handsome, dark-haired, vivid Bob Gann, whom Whittaker had liked so much, who had confided in him, and who was beginning to fade as memory always faded.

It had been a long, long day; they had lived a lifetime in it.

'Please,' Pirran muttered brokenly, 'please, I have told you all I can—everything. Don't hurt me! Don't hurt me!'

Whittaker said briskly:

'All right, Pirran, you can have another chance. But don't forget what can happen if you throw it away. What was in the packet?'

'I have told you,' Pirran said and gulped. 'Diamonds; a fortune in diamonds. They were from a famous dealer in Amsterdam, and Camponi stole them.' He gulped again, 'And I stole them from Camponi! That was why he attacked me, why I was in such danger. I needed help desperately. You and Gann. . . .'

'You had the nerve to have an F.B.I. man protect you with a fortune in stolen jewels in your possession?' Whittaker demanded incredulously.

It was so fantastic that surely no one could have invented such a story.

Pirran said hoarsely: 'Gann didn't know. Camponi dared not tell him! I believed I was safe with you and Gann, but you know what followed. Maisie made that deal with me, and——'

Whittaker broke in, 'Did she drug you?'

Pirran said: 'I can't be sure. I can't be sure she didn't double-cross me. But Camponi killed her, so . . .' Pirran broke off; his lips worked his eyes became very bright. 'Whittaker, if Maisie drugged me and stole the packet but didn't tell him, no wonder he killed her!' He moistened his lips, and muttered, 'Please, a little water—a little water,' he muttered.

'I'll get it,' Eve said. She got up and was soon back with a glass of water. Pirran kept licking his lips in anticipation, yet when he drank he drooled. He was obviously a terrified and beaten man.

Would he lie now—or keep anything back?

'Thank you,' he said; 'thank you very much.' He wiped his mouth with the back of his hand. 'Whittaker, you can do what you like. You cannot get any more out of me, because that is all I can tell you. This story of Camponi's? Perhaps he believed you and Gann knew where the real packet was; if he thought that I did, then he could believe that I had told you. But—I know nothing more.'

He paused and looked at Whittaker from eyes which were

not only colourless, but without any life or vitality at all.

Whittaker said, 'I don't believe that Camponi or anyone else would kill because a man *might* know something dangerous.'

Pirran shrugged helplessly, pathetically.

'I can't explain more,' he said. 'I cannot even guess. Whichever way I look, there's trouble. You think I have the diamonds. So does Ricky. . . .'

He stopped.

Eve didn't speak, but Whittaker saw the way she looked at him when Pirran mentioned the diamonds this time. Before, she had been surprised and puzzled; now, she had had time to think, to realise that Whittaker had know about them, but hadn't confided in her. Would this mar the strange idyll of their day?

'There is *nothing* more,' Pirran repeated with emphasis, born out of fear. 'I know nothing more at all.'

Eve got up and walked across the room, then sat down at the piano and stared at a photograph. Whittaker couldn't see the face in the photograph, but he felt sure that if it were turned towards him he would see Bob Gann.

He made himself say: 'A man came to shoot Mrs. Gann. He said that Ricky sent him.' There was a pause while he stared at Pirran. Then, 'He was in your apartment at the hotel.'

'So—is that my fault?' asked Pirran, and his arms flopped. 'Didn't I tell you, Ricky left him with me. I know he had been out on some other job. What job—how should I know?' He looked blankly at Whittaker, and then showed a flicker of interest. His face perked up: a fish coming to life again. '*What* is that? He *told* you he came from Ricky?'

'Yes.'

'No man who came from Ricky would dare to name him,' Pirran declared. 'He worked for Ricky, I know about that, but if he named him he double-crossed him! Who would he be working for?' That squeak came back into the man's voice. 'Can you tell me?'

Whittaker didn't answer.

'Who stole the packet? Was it Maisie? Did she manage to get it from me or from Camponi? Did she substitute the one that was empty for the one he had found?' Now, Pirran's voice was shrill. 'Did Maisie have it, and did she give it to

the other girl, the quiet girl—what was her name—Olive?
Yes, Olive Johns. That's the one you want—not me! Does
she know?'

Could she?

Whittaker found his heart racing at the thought.

Blick had gone to see Olive Johns, so obviously Ricky had
suspected her. She might have lied, might have fooled
Whittaker, and still be sitting on that fortune.

*   *   *

Whittaker called the Lamprey Hotel.
Olive Johns was still in room 35.

CHAPTER XVII

'DON'T GO!'

EVE stood a little way from the telephone, quite still, looking
at Whittaker. Her head was raised. If she had been carved
out of some rock which throbbed with the blood of woman,
she could not have looked more beautiful. She did not say
a word, and yet she called him. The depth of the tragedy
was in her eyes, and yet there was a light too, and desperation. The dead were all around her, yet now it was clear
that her concern was for the living.

She knew what Whittaker would do.

She knew, although they had not met until the dawning of
the previous day, that he would go to the Lamprey Hotel,
to find out what he could of Olive Johns.

It was as inevitable as night following day, and yet she
could not have known it; could only have divined it as she
saw Whittaker put down the receiver. He had not even said
that Olive was still there.

He found himself looking at Eve with tension in his eyes
and body.

Pirran was not with them now, but locked in a closet, in a
lounge chair which gave him some comfort, communing
with himself and his past sins and present fears. He might
never have existed.

127

'Neil,' Eve said, 'don't go!'

He didn't answer.

'They'll be waiting for you,' she said. 'They know that you'll get round to her before long, and all they have to do is wait. That's why they're not here. That's why they weren't at Rachel's apartment. Neil, I beg you not to go.'

He could lie to her.

In fact he knew that he could not lie successfully; he could not bring himself to lie—to try to cheat her. The truth lay between them, and it must always be like that.

'I must go,' he said quietly. 'It is the only thing to do.'

She drew a deep breath.

She still seemed to be pleading with him silently, and to be calling him. The simple, the easy thing would be to step towards her and take her in his arms and—*forget*. His heart beat with a fierce, challenging force. *Take her, take her, take her* seemed to be a refrain beating itself against his mind and against his lips. It could turn him mad. It could make him forget Bob Gann. It could make him forget that if he once moved towards her, once put his arms about her, he would forfeit not only all her respect, but any hope of her the future might hold. But he had to fight with himself. He had to remind himself that her anxiety was desperate because of her grief. Bob had died, and the fear that he would also die made her fight for his life. She had no chance to fight for Bob's.

'Eve, don't you see,' Whittaker made himself say, 'I must go. If Olive——'

'I can see,' she said, and there was a throbbing note of bitterness in her voice. 'Oh, I can see what you're going to do. You're going to do what Bob did—you're going to kill yourself. Time and time and time again I told him, I warned him, that he must stop. A man can tempt death too often; Bob tempted it every day of his life, and why—*why*? Oh, he could find fine words. His duty, his job, his country, his conscience—any one or all of them would go before his wife and children. Did he owe *nothing* to them? He behaved as if they didn't exist, when he was away from us. He was always looking for death, looking for a way of making us writhe with the agony of knowing he might never come back. What do you think happened to me when you told me he was dead? The thing I had been expecting for an age had happened, and I tell you that something in me died. What will happen to Mimi, when she knows? To Bob? Why, Bob worshipped him! To Bob, his father was——'

She stopped, as if the words and the thoughts choked her; and still Whittaker did not move.

Tears glistened in her eyes, as if they had been wrung from the very depth of her being. She stood less upright, and her hands moved a little, as if subconsciously she wanted to find something to touch, to hold on to.

Whittaker did nothing to help her, felt as if he himself had been turned to stone. One false move, now, and all hopes would be in ruins.

He must not touch her, for her body would send the fire raging through his veins.

'I'm sorry,' Eve said huskily, brokenly. 'I'm sorry I talked like that. But—why must you get *yourself* killed? You only knew Bob for a few days. It's not your country. It's not your affair. You were to help to keep Pirran alive, and he's alive and being looked after, isn't he?' The wryness of that made her lips twist, as if a smile were forcing itself through against everything she wanted to do. 'Why don't you stop looking? Why don't you go back to England? Tell the police here the truth of it, and go while you're alive.'

'If I go,' said Whittaker, 'how shall I remember you?'

'If you die how will you remember anyone?' The tension was back, her moment of weakness gone. 'Nothing need keep you here. You've made Pirran talk, you've found that Olive must be involved; in twenty-four hours or a little more you've done as you dared to hope. Why don't you stop before it's too late, before you're slaughtered, too?'

'Eve,' Whittaker said, 'I must go.'

She raised her hands again and looked at him for a long time; and then, with a catch in her voice, she turned away.

He remembered the first time that he had seen her going up the stairs. The slow, stiff movements, only hinting at grace while talking of grief. He remembered how she had looked when he had told her what had happened to her husband. He could hear other sounds, as if the child Mimi were playing in the garden; as if it were daylight, not dark night.

He watched her.

She disappeared.

This was the time when he should go. Out of the house, to the car, into Manhattan, along Broadway, into the Lamprey Hotel. He hadn't started thinking about how he would get in there, yet, or what he wanted to do. Search the apartment? Try to force Olive to talk? From the time that she had screamed to the police he had been sure she wasn't all she had seemed. . . .

Never mind Olive; forget Olive. *Think*.

Whittaker looked towards the empty landing. He heard no movement above his head, although he saw a light go on. He wished she would come down. He longed for Eve to understand the compulsion which drove him.

Of course, she did.

She had understood with Bob, too, and hated it. She was right in believing that Bob had driven himself to his own death. There was a time when a man should stop, where one's own life was more important than the shadowy things of living, the abstracts of duty. He knew what she had tried to say; what all the women of such men would always try to say. There came a moment when logic and reason vanished; when a man like him, like Bob, was driven under a driving compulsion which he simply couldn't control. He found names and excuses for it, he could make up reasons, if he were called upon to speak to the multitudes gathered in the market place he could make himself out a hero, but— what was the truth?

Wasn't Eve right?

She was upstairs, fighting her bitterness alone.

He stayed down here, fighting the unseen forces, thinking now of Olive Johns, of Bob—with the back of his head a dreadful sight—of all the things that had happened and all the powers which were fighting each other. Pirran and Rickett, both evil men, using the powers of corruption to have their own way.

And—the packet.

Where was it?

Were diamonds its only secret?

Rickett wanted it, Pirran had wanted it, someone unknown had stolen it. Rickett was fighting for it, and had believed Pirran when he had sworn that it had been taken from him. There was the man who had gone to Olive, to search, who had started searching, and whom he, Whittaker, had stop-

130

ped. He was in the hands of the police, now—what else could he have wanted but news of the packet?

Suddenly he knew that he would have to go.

He stood by the open door of the room upstairs. He heard no sound of movement; but for the light that streamed through, he would not have been sure that this was the room she had entered. He had come upstairs slowly, because he knew that he must go into New York, but first he had to tell Eve; he had to try to make her understand that it went deeper than any sense of duty, it was part of existence.

He knew that he was confessing to weakness by going upstairs.

He should have left her without another word.

No, that was wrong, he shouldn't leave her; he couldn't go without giving her a chance to come with him. She might be in danger. There was no way of being sure that the house wasn't being watched, the only certain thing was that no watchers had yet moved in.

He called 'Eve' in a quiet voice.

She didn't answer.

'Eve,' he said.

'Why don't you go?' she asked in a slow voice. 'Nothing I can say or do can make you stay.'

'Eve, I want you to come with me, part of the way.'

'I shall stay here.'

'There might be danger here.'

'Does that really matter?' she asked bitterly. 'Do you really care? Aren't you saying that just to square your conscience, and in the hope that when you're dead, I'll remember that you pretended that you would like to help me?'

'Eve,' Whittaker said, and thrust the door open, 'this is your fight as much as mine. Remember?' He strode into the room, touched with an anger he hadn't intended, which welled up out of nowhere. 'You wanted to avenge Bob, you——'

He stopped as if the words had been sliced from his lips with a knife.

She was so very lovely, now, and tragedy was in her loveliness too.

He stood with one leg slightly forward of the other, his hands raised as he had pushed them forward in a kind of

131

angry appeal. He looked at her as she sat by the dressing-table. There she was, in all her beauty, with a wrap loosely around her. Her limbs were so straight and the lines so clean; all of her was so lovely, too.

She wasn't smiling; her eyes held a despairing glow.

'Neil,' she whispered, 'don't go; I beg you not to go.'

He didn't move.

'Neil,' she said, 'don't do what Bob did, don't kill yourself, for him or for me or for money. Today and tomorrow and all the tomorrows we can be alive; let's not have more things to mourn. Don't go!'

Whittaker's teeth were clamped together, and he could feel the sweat on his forehead, the clammy tightness at the back of his neck, at the palm of his hands. He looked at her as if he meant to carry the picture for all the days of his life. He felt the pressure of his jaws, and the demand of his own body, but——

He turned away.

*   *   *

'Eve,' he said, from the other side of the door, 'I want you to come with me. I'll wait in the car for twenty minutes or so. Time for you to get ready.'

She didn't answer.

He went downstairs and out into the night, which might be filled with watching eyes. He had forgotten Olive Johns, Pirran, Ricky, all the deadly things that had happened, all the menace that New York held for him.

He could only think of Eve.

*   *   *

Whittaker sat waiting, the second cigarette nearly smoked, the night for company, the distant lights showing the shadowy branches of the trees, and the fragile leaves which, in the sun, had their own beauty. He heard the mosquitoes humming, inside the car; and the rustling sounds of the night, and the never-still engines on the highways and in the sky.

It was nearly half an hour since he had left the house.

The lights still shone there.

He found himself thinking, blindly, that she wasn't coming, that he would never see her again. She was calling him back as clearly now as she had before. She was telling him that there was nothing, *nothing in this world*, that she would not do to save his life.

Then a light in the house went out.

Another.

Soon he heard her coming.

*   *   *

And no one watched.

CHAPTER XVIII

OLIVE AGAIN

WHITTAKER leaned across and opened the door, and Eve got in beside him. There was so little light that all he saw was the movement of her slim legs, and the outline of her white glove. Neither of them spoke. He let in the clutch and started off, fighting to make sure that he drove well and didn't stab at the controls. They swayed up the hill towards the main street, and he remembered the directions well enough to turn towards New York without being told which way. The silence went on, and there seemed no easy way of breaking it; yet it had to be broken. The wrong word would be disastrous and he knew that.

He turned into the parkway.

The traffic wasn't thick, but there was enough coming in each direction to make him think. He didn't want to think. His mind and his heart were in turmoil, and as the silence dragged out he began to be afraid of it—as if it were some monstrous, shapeless Thing which could not be seen, could not be brought to grips.

A long way ahead the sky was bright with the lights of the city.

'Eve,' said Whittaker.

She didn't answer.

'Eve,' said Whittaker, 'now and for ever—thank you for not staying behind.'

She didn't move and didn't speak. He thought, in distress,

133

that it had been no good, he had not struck the right note and had not helped her. But soon there was a perceptible change; he could hear her breathing more normally, she wasn't quite so tense. He began to hope again and drove more slowly.

'Neil,' she said at last, 'how do you intend to get into the hotel?'

'To tell you the truth,' answered Whittaker, 'I haven't given it much thought. The occasion usually creates the method.' He spoke with ridiculous care, was almost precise, in his anxiety to say nothing to distress or disturb her. 'I've a face that loses itself in a crowd.'

'You ought to have some kind of disguise,' Eve said. 'You *must* have.'

'I've always got through.'

'You might not, this time. If the police suspect Olive Johns, they'll be watching. So will Ricky's men.' She was very matter-of-fact.

'I don't carry make-up, because I've never used it,' Whittaker said.

'Bob had some things,' Eve told him in a taut, high-pitched voice. 'I've brought them.'

*   *   *

She had brought rubber cheek-pads to make Whittaker's face look fuller, nasal pads which would thicken his nose, gum to tighten the skin at his eyes and lips. As he put them on, using her mirror, he felt the real desperation of her desire to make sure he didn't die.

When he had finished he looked at her and said:

'You're magnificent, Eve. One day I'll say thanks.'

He paused, but only for a moment. 'If you'll book a double room and say I'm coming later with the luggage, I can come in after you've moved in. I'm not likely to be stopped while walking to the lift. The night staff didn't see me last time.'

'That sounds reasonable,' Eve conceded.

'It ought to work,' Whittaker said. 'The experts always say that the simple way is the best, it's the obvious course the other side wouldn't expect you to take.'

She didn't respond, but he sensed the way she relaxed. He took a packet of cigarettes from his pocket and handed

134

it to her. She lit one and put it to his lips. He drew on it, but didn't speak beyond a murmured 'Thanks'. It was all that was needed. He felt not only the warmth of the evening but of their new companionable quiet. It was like being at peace; he reminded himself that he hadn't known anything like it for a long, long time.

'If we have any luck,' he added, 'I can park near the hotel.'

'Not too near,' she warned. 'Where is it?'

'Broadway at 61st.'

'Park on the other side of Tenth Avenue,' Eve advised. 'There's more room, and you would probably get a place where you could drive off in a hurry.'

'Fine!'

New York. . . .

At the beginning of a built-up area, it was dark except for just the street lights and a few lighted windows, but gradually the lights ahead lured them and spread about them, and soon they drove through a blazing sea of neon, with all the other traffic and the people like actors in a huge, spot-lighted stage. Whittaker turned off Broadway towards Tenth, along a one-way street, leading and crossed Tenth; right at the corner across the road was a space to park; he could reverse and be off in a few seconds, for there was no room for anyone to park behind him.

'Perfect,' he said.

'Don't get out yet,' said Eve. 'When you're inside the hotel, what are you going to do?'

'Have a little talk with Olive.'

'You haven't forgotten that they probably expect you?'

'I haven't forgotten anything.'

'All right,' Eve said. 'Let's go.'

He wondered what she was really thinking. He had seen how magnificently she could control her thoughts, and thrust her feelings out of the way. Was she doing that now? They walked briskly away from the river and the slight breeze it offered, towards the hotel. Its illuminated sign blazed in dazzling red: *Hotel Lamprey*. He could see the window of the room he had occupied. Since he had come to New York, he seemed to have been on the move every moment, to have had a dozen temporary sanctuaries.

'I'll go into the restaurant, and have a drink,' he said.

135

'It's pretty dark in there. Come in through the entrance from the hotel.'

'Surely.'

The street entrance to the restaurant was twenty yards from the main entrance to the hotel. Whittaker left Eve. She hardly paused as she went on. He forced himself to go into the restaurant, and not to wait until she was out of sight. Only a wall and a few tables separated them, but it seemed like a wall.

A dark-clad head-waiter appeared out of the gloom of the dimly-lit restaurant. In a far corner a fleshy blonde was crooning and swaying in a strapless gown, and behind her a pianist drooped over the keys of a piano that was slightly out of tune.

'Just for one, sir?' He had a slight accent.

'I'll have a drink,' Whittaker said. 'I'm waiting for a friend.'

'Ver-ee good, sir. The bar iss dere.'

No one could miss the bar. One man sat at it, his head buried in his hands, another was beating time to the crooning with a swizzle stick against a glass, a couple sat close together at the far end. The barman seemed to be waiting for dynamite to liven the place up. Whittaker pulled up a stool, and the man sauntered over.

'Tom Collins,' he said.

'Sure.'

A pause, and some juggling.

'Thanks.'

Whittaker was very sensitive to time, more so than usual tonight. He seemed to have been waiting for Eve all day. Now, he waited ten minutes, and it was an age. The old, familiar thumping at his heart came back, and he fought against it, tried to make his drink last out, but finally finished it and ordered another. The crooner stopped; only the pianist could be heard now in a listless melody.

Where was Eve?

She wouldn't stand him up, would she? He knew that she wouldn't, but that didn't satisfy him. She wouldn't let him down willingly, but remember what she had been prepared to do, simply to keep him away from here. She had come to him of her own accord, and he had taken it for granted that it meant she had submitted to his compulsion. But had she?

136

Had she fooled him?

Twenty minutes.

She didn't need twenty minutes to book a room, and to come in here. Five or ten was needed at most. Even if she went to see the room—and she wouldn't do that, or she needn't do it—she was too long.

Half an hour.

He stubbed out his third cigarette, and moved away from the bar. No one took any notice of him, not even the smooth head-waiter. He went into the hotel. Two elderly women, one nursing a small, fluffy dog, were sitting in a corner and leaning forward as they talked. A very tall man, wearing a ten-gallon hat, and with an overnight case by the side of his chair, lay back in the chair with his long legs stretched out, and mouth slightly open as he slept. A man whom he hadn't seen before was at the desk.

Whittaker nodded.

The man said 'Hi,' and then a buzzer sounded, and he turned to the telephone. 'Hotel Lamprey. . . .'

The lift doors were closed. Whittaker pressed one button and heard the lift humming. Out of the corner of his eye he watched the clerk. The man seemed to have taken no action, but he might be playing dumb.

The lift came down and the doors opened.

Whittaker stepped in and pressed button 1. He couldn't get to the first floor quick enough, not out of it as soon as he wished. He went down the stairs as swiftly as he had the previous day, and opened the doors leading into the entrance hall a few inches. He could just see the clerk's head. The man was totting up some figures; he wasn't at the telephone, and didn't look in the slightest degree alarmed.

Whittaker drew back.

He went to the lift at the first floor, and this time pressed for the third. He stepped on to the familiar landing half expecting to see a man, like his prisoner of the morning, or like the one who had been here when he had first arrived.

No one was here.

What was the matter with Ricky?

Even if the police had decided that Olive knew nothing, what was Ricky doing?

Whittaker moved towards room 34. He was sure of one thing: that Eve had not needed all the time she had taken,

137

and that she had come here to do what she could by herself. It was just another form of sacrifice.

He reached the door and listened.

He heard a sharp slap of sound, and then the murmur of a man's voice.

Whittaker couldn't catch the words and didn't hear anything else for several seconds; but suddenly that slapping sound was repeated. A man was slapping a woman across the face, and then asking questions. He tried the handle of the door, and pushed; the door was locked, of course it would be. He turned it again, and then put his shoulder to it. There was no sound outside, not even the hum of the elevator.

Then came blessed noise.

That was his first thought about it. Radio music blared out inside the room, drowning any sound he made. He tensed himself to thrust at the door—but before he did so, he saw the other possible reason for that radio blaring: that it would drown any sound made inside the room.

He took out his skeleton key and made himself move cautiously; every nerve was strained. The lock turned, making hardly a sound. He opened the door just an inch, and peered into the room. The music blaring at him from a radio was deafening. Music drowned all sound, but didn't do anything from stopping him from seeing the thing that was happening in here.

Olive, by the bed, near the radio; dressed.

At the foot of the bed a man with a cigarette in his hand—held oddly, not as if he were going to draw at it but as if he were going to stab with it.

Eve, thrust back against the wardrobe, her dress ripped down off one shoulder, her creamy skin bared to the glowing heat of the end of the cigarette.

No one moved.

*   *   *

No one moved for the split second which followed; there was just the blaring of the radio, and now Whittaker knew that it had been switched on to drown the sound of any scream that Eve should make.

Then *he* moved, and the man heard the door open.

He reached the man, who dropped the cigarette and snatched at his gun. It was Blick. No man living could have

138

reached his pocket in time. The blow lifted him off his feet and over the foot of the bed. His legs reared up in the air, as if he were going to turn a somersault; but he didn't; his legs came down again, like a branch of a tree suddenly lopped off.

Whittaker turned swiftly, closed the door, and although it snapped, it made little sound and it would cut off the noise the radio was making. In the same swift movement he took a chair and thrust it behind the door, so that the back caught beneath the handle, and there was no risk of the door opening suddenly.

He turned to Olive Johns.

'Turn it down a bit, Olive,' he said, 'I can't hear myself speak.' Olive, crouching, didn't move and didn't say a word.

Eve, shrugging her dress back on to her shoulder, walked past Whittaker without looking at him, reached the radio and turned it down; the music was still loud and clear, but much quieter than it had been.

Then she looked at Whittaker.

'I'd started to question her when the man came in; he must have been next door. He wanted to know where you were.'

'Did Olive say anything?' Whittaker asked flatly.

Very slowly, Eve answered, 'Not yet.'

'Too bad,' he said. 'Much too bad. Eve, get a pin from the dressing-table, pin up that dress of yours, and then go and wait for me at the car.'

He wondered if he had asked too much.

She had always intended to come and do what she could by herself, of course, and he had been a blind fool not to realise that. He didn't blame her. He would always have profound admiration for her, and this would be one of the things that would stand out. Her courage and her determination.

It was easy to forget that it was her fight. He, not Eve, was the interloper. He couldn't and he didn't blame her for what she had done, but as he told himself that he may have asked too much, he wondered what he would do if she refused.

CHAPTER XIX

'WITH LOVE, HONEY'

THERE wasn't any time to play with. The noise might have disturbed others, nearby; the clerk might have fooled Whittaker, Blick might have friends at hand. There just wasn't time to argue with Eve. He knew that when he left he might have to leave in a hurry, and that if the two of them were here it might lose fatal time.

Only a second or two passed after he asked her to wait in the car, but they were precious. He wanted to shout at her, but he restrained himself.

'I'll be in room 71,' she said at last. 'I couldn't get one any nearer. I'll repair the dress up there.'

'If I'm not with you in half an hour, you get away,' he insisted.

'All right,' she said flatly.

She went out, moving the chair so as to open the door. He put it back in position. The man was still lying full-length on the bed, half-conscious. His hands were in sight. Whittaker went to him, took the gun from his shoulder holster, and actually laughed as he put it into his pocket. Three! Then he found more cotton wool, and plugged Blick's ears.

He moved about the room, watching Olive, opening a drawer here, another there. All her things were unpacked. He kept looking at her, hoping to see some sign that she was nervous of what he might find, but she took no notice at all—until he touched a photograph which lay in a drawer, face downwards.

Whittaker sensed her sharpening interest.

He picked the photograph up and turned it over. It was of Bob Gann, and a fine one, showing him at his handsome best. Across it in his writing was written: '*For Olive, with love, Honey.*'

Whittaker didn't look up at once. Olive Johns wasn't even remotely demure or quiet, now. She leaned against the wall with her shoulders drooping, her hair flopping over her forehead and over one eye. Her mouth was slightly open, and she was panting for breath. That as much from shock as from anything else. It didn't make her look pretty; in fact, it turned her ugly—slatternly. For the first time he could see something of the real nature of Olive Johns. There had been a time when he had thought that what she needed was a sound spanking, but it went far, far deeper than that. She was bad; gone rotten. What had happened on board the *Queen B.* had been coldly and calculatedly done; that body, a snare.

She wasn't the only one who knew its power.

Whittaker's teeth gritted against one another so tightly that his jaws hurt. He dare not be side-tracked; dare not let himself think about the significance of Bob Gann signing a picture for Olive Johns.

'Olive,' he said, 'so far I've been gentle with you.'

She tossed her head back, and her hair with it. She didn't move from the position near the radio. Her glowing eyes, dark and velvety brown, told him now how much she hated him for coming here; for doing what he had.

'Just tell me where the packet is,' he said.

'If I knew where it was,' said Olive Johns, 'I'd throw it into the Hudson River before I'd let you touch it.'

'You know. And you can get hurt, too.'

'I don't know where it is,' she said. 'Take that or leave it. I don't know.'

'You took it from Maisie.'

'That's right,' she said, and gave a sneering laugh. 'I took it from Maisie all right—and she took it from Bob.'

Bob.

'What did you do with it?'

'It was collected.'

'By whom?'

'Whittaker,' Olive said with soft venom, 'even if I knew I wouldn't tell you. Not now, not any time.'

He believed that she meant it.

He believed, also, that he could make her talk: it was one thing for her to be brave, while she doubted whether he would hurt her enough to make her talk. But if once she came to believe that he would be ruthless, she might crack. He had to make her crack. He was near the truth, and he sensed that as he had never sensed it before.

'Olive,' he said, 'I'm not soft-hearted, or thin-skinned.'

'Neil,' she sneered, 'you aren't going to do a thing to me. I don't know who she was; I just gave her the packet, as Bob asked me to.'

141

He couldn't keep back: '*She?*'

Olive gave a scornful laugh; as if in spite of the danger, and what had happened, she could get a kick out of this.

'That's right,' she said. 'Another woman in the case—*Bob's* other woman.'

'Bob's' echoed in his mind, and for a moment he felt sick and stupid. She couldn't mean what she seemed to mean. Take it apart. This was the second time she had talked of Bob as if she were on intimate terms with him. She could pretend, but why should she?

'And that's all I know,' she said clearly. 'That's all I know about the packet now. Shall I tell you some other things, *Neil* honey?—for instance, what a fool Bob made of you?'

He thought: 'No,' but he didn't speak, and didn't look away from her. She was doing something which she probably didn't intend: making him angry. She was sowing the seeds of doubt and mistrust in his mind, and that wasn't healthy, because his own nerves and emotions were too raw to stand much of it. He could easily lose control.

'*Bob* took the packet from Maisie,' Olive said, 'and he handed it over to me. It meant big money, and he knew what to do with it. Bob fixed it with Maisie and me, told us to string along with Pirran. He got the real packet two days before Camponi acted—and wasn't Camponi mad . . .!' She paused, as if to make sure that it all sank in; that it hurt as much as anything of the kind could hurt.

Whittaker didn't speak.

The man on the bed stirred, but made no attempt to get off. Whittaker was within arm's reach of him and could flatten him at a single blow, just as he could this girl. He could even break her pretty neck. One swift, savage blow, and he could snap it in two. He felt as if he wanted to.

Olive said: 'You work hard on this, Neil, and where will it get you? Want *her* to know that Bob Gann wasn't straight?'

He had sent Eve away, as if driven by a premonition of all this. It was something he would be glad about for the rest of his days.

Olive put her hands to her forehead and thrust them backwards, drawing the glossy dark hair back tightly, throwing her face into sharp relief. There was nothing remotely demure or quiet about her; there was a wantonness no man could ever mistake; and there was desire to hurt, too; he could feel it as surely as if she had a knife blade in him, twisting and twisting.

'That's the way it was,' she said. 'Bob had slaved all his life for pin-money and couldn't wait any longer for a big chance. The diamonds were too big for him. He knew it all: that Camponi stole them, operating for Ricky; Pirran took them from Camponi; and Maisie and I were to help Camponi get them back. But we preferred to work with Bob. I wouldn't lie to you, Neil *honey*. Bob told me who would collect the diamonds in New York, someone who would hold them until they cooled off. And—she collected.'

'And you didn't know her?' Whittaker asked in a hard voice.

'She gave me half of a photograph of Bob. He'd given me the other.' Olive pointed. 'Go and see; it's in that drawer.'

It was in a drawer beneath Bob's photograph. He found the two halves, and there was Bob Gann, handsome, easy, smiling. He wanted to tear the pieces across and across, but stopped himself from that as well as from showing any emotion at all.

'What was she like?'

'She had two legs, two arms. . . .'

'Olive,' he said, 'don't take too many chances.'

She stopped, for the tone of his voice and the look in his eyes had scared her.

'What was there between you and Bob?' he made himself say.

She didn't answer, until he rasped:

'Come on, let's have it!'

'Don't come any nearer,' Olive said urgently. 'Don't!' He stood where he was, watching and hating her, as she went on: 'We'd met in London, when Bob found out that Maisie and I were with Camponi. He'd been away from home for a long time, and he—he wanted someone who'd give——'

She stopped. Then:

'If you don't believe me,' she said, 'look at that photograph. But don't get it wrong. He told me he'd rather kill me than let me wreck his home. But *you'd* wreck it, wouldn't you? You have to drag out all the truth!'

She still gripped her head between her hands, the scarlet nails like blobs of blood against the dark hair. Suddenly she threw back her head and screamed laughter at him, as if she

143

wanted to go on gloating until his breath died away.

The music droned on.

The man on the bed stirred.

What was the use of arguing? Whittaker asked himself. Of course it was true. There was no point in her lying. London —and later Bob—had wanted that packet, and had got it. He had used her as his messenger, and she had given it to 'his woman'—no, wait!

'Olive,' Whittaker said, 'why give up a fortune when Bob was dead?'

'Oh, she paid me,' Olive said, swiftly. 'And what good were they to me? With Ricky on one side and the police on the other, I wouldn't have had a chance—not a chance in a million! So I collected ten thousand dollars, and was glad to.'

Whittaker didn't consciously think, 'Eve?' He wouldn't let himself. He was sure that when the moment of shock was gone, and he could see more clearly, he would realise that it couldn't have been her.

Bob Gann had fooled him, though; completely.

'He was worried about you,' Olive was saying, hoarsely. 'He thought Pirran had arranged for you to spy on him, thought you might guess what he was up to. I told him he needn't worry, told him you were a blind fool, but he was still worried.'

Whittaker said very softly, 'Who is she, Olive?'

'I couldn't tell you that,' she said, and her voice quivered, as if she had trouble in controlling it. 'I couldn't tell you or anyone in this world, even if I wanted to. Ricky tried to make me tell. *Blick's* from Ricky. Ask him!' She stabbed a finger towards the man on the bed. 'They've tried everything, but I can't tell. I didn't want to know; if I knew, it would put me on the spot. So I collected, and that's all. I guessed I'd have a few bad days. But when everyone realised I didn't know her——'

'What was she like?'

'She wore a veil, and she hardly said a word. I can't tell you a thing more.'

Whittaker said: 'Listen. Bob Gann had a reputation. Perhaps he betrayed it. Perhaps he betrayed all the trust that was put in him, but it doesn't alter the fact that he had a reputation for being on the square. So——'

'Should I care now?'

'Yes, you should care, because that reputation will die if the truth is told. But if I can get the packet——'

'No,' she said swiftly, 'you can't fool me like that, you can't twist the words round. Bob asked me to give it to her, and I did.'

She drew back slowly, giving Whittaker the impression that the strength had drained out of her. He stood watching. He hadn't reached the stage of wondering what would happen if Eve ever learned the truth about Bob. He didn't want to face that. He wanted those diamonds, and wanted to find out who worked with Bob, who the mysterious woman was. He wanted Ricky, too, but Ricky could wait. This unknown woman was the cog on which all this violence and all the murders had turned. It was all-important.

'Olive,' Whittaker said, 'there are two ways of doing this: the hard and the easy. I believe you know more. Tell me, and you'll get away with all the rest. I won't tell the police where I got the information. If you need more money, I'll see that you get it. I'll see you through. But if you won't tell me who took the packet, then you'll get the whole works. First from me—and if I can't break you, then from the police. . . .'

'No one in the world could break me,' she screeched, and flung herself bodily at him.

He should have expected it, but he hadn't.

She launched herself forward like a stone from a catapult —a stone with sharp, razor-like edges. She clawed at his face, at his eyes, at his mouth. He tasted the salt of blood. She kicked at him and butted at him with her head, as if she had gone completely mad. For the first few seconds he had to give ground, could concentrate only on defending himself and saving his eyes. He fought for just a breathing-space, for this fury couldn't last. If he hadn't been so pent-up with the other things it would never have happened.

He held her off.

She still raged, but she couldn't get at him.

Then the man on the bed rolled over, leapt off the bed and grabbed the chair from the door. Whittaker couldn't stop him; it all happened in a split second. He tried to push the maddened woman off, but she clung to him. He couldn't even turn round. He knew that the chair was poised above

145

his head, that the man meant to kill him. He hadn't a chance while Olive clung like a leech; and death could come any second, any——

He made a tremendous effort, and spun round with the woman in his arms.

Blick brought the chair crashing down, and one leg caught Olive's head.

Whittaker heard the crunch. He saw her eyes roll. He heard the sound which he had once feigned, only a few yards from this very spot. He felt her relax, and saw her fold up.

Blick was nearly off his balance, but struck again. Whittaker flung his left arm up to fend off the blow. A leg of the chair smashed against him; a bone seemed to crack. His arm dropped, lifeless, and he couldn't dodge away because of Olive Johns in a crumpled heap; he saw the chair raised in the man's two hands, saw it falling, knew that it was smashing towards the back of his head.

He collapsed.

He fell a fraction of a second before the blow came, and by dropping, robbed it of some of its force. But he couldn't stop himself from falling, he couldn't save himself if there were another blow.

The chair smashed on the floor and broke.

There was a moment's pause.

He heard running footsteps, then the radio music, gay and lilting, with a bright-voiced vocalist saying: '*Oh, gee! it's a wonderful wonderful wonderful world.*'

Blick had run off in panic.

Was Olive dead?

Would *he* live?

CHAPTER XX

THE PHOTOGRAPH

WHITTAKER could hardly see. His head felt as if great wheels were inside it, grinding round and round, smashing at his nerves and making them scream. There were spots and vivid flashes in front of his eyes. His right arm was aching badly;

146

he didn't think much about it, because it all seemed part of the same pain, the same hopelessness. Something within him told him to hurry, but he could not; he did not think he could move without help.

Someone was singing.

'Oh, gee! it's a wonderful wonderful wonderful world.'

A man started speaking, and the music faded into the background. The man's voice was very persuasive, and he seemed to be trying to raise a laugh. The only effect on Whittaker was to make him try to raise his head.

There was—Olive.

Bob Gann; Maisie Gregson; Olive Johns. They had all died in the same way; seeing the one with the savaged head was like seeing them all.

'There's no doubt about it, folks, the finest washing machine in this wonderful wonderful wonderful world. Why, you could say that it's because of the Instanto washing machine that it IS a wonderful wonderful world! And, remember, there's no obligation if you would like to try this wonderful machine in your own home. All you have to do . . .'

Whittaker got to his knees.

He heard a different sound, without knowing what it was. He put a hand to his forehead, and felt it warm and sticky. His right arm wouldn't move freely. When he raised it as high as his shoulder, pain streaked through it, but he didn't think of 'broken'—it was just part of all the rest of the pain.

The girl started singing:

'Oh, gee! It's a wonderful wonderful . . .'

A man bellowed from outside, 'Do you want to shut that door or do you want me to come and shut it for you?'

Whittaker thought, 'What door?'

Then he realised that the passage door was ajar, and that the caller was someone from one of the other rooms. The door was a long way out of his reach, and the man sounded as if he were drawing near. Whittaker got unsteadily to his feet and made himself cry:

'Sorry! Sorry, a friend went out . . .'

He staggered towards the door and pushed it; it slammed. He didn't stop to think that it might also enrage the man who had reached the threshold. He moved as swiftly as he could and switched off the radio: luck made him turn the right dial in the right direction. The silence was like a benediction.

'. . . That's better!' the man shouted. 'Keep it that way!' He stumped off.

Whittaker looked down at the girl's body and closed his eyes. He felt sick, but went to her and felt her pulse. There wasn't a sign of life. Her head was a hideous sight.

He turned away, and after a while wondered what he himself looked like. He thought of Eve, and there was another reason for dread: what would happen when she knew?

Need she ever know?

Not about Olive, anyway; he could stop her from knowing about Olive, couldn't he? Destroy that photograph, and how could she find out? Vaguely, he thought of the man who had heard everything she had said, and who could tell Eve—but why should he? And what use were words? That photograph with the message of love was one piece of finite evidence which nothing could deny.

There it lay.

He managed to reach it and stand up with it. It swayed in his hand; *he* was swaying. He put it down and picked up a box of matches lying beside it. He tore off a match, and tried to strike it; the head broke off. He tried another, and the flame burnt his fingers. He winced, and dropped it, and the match fell on the photograph, on to the middle of Bob Gann's forehead. That was all right. The third match flared normally, and he held it to a corner of the photograph until the print began to flame. He picked it up by another corner, and, holding it downwards so that the flame would spread, went unsteadily into the bathroom. He stood over the shower well, letting the flames lick around the photographs. Bob's chin and mouth, his nose and eyes, began to blister in the heat, then to smoke, then to spurt flames. The wording perished. Whittaker held just a corner of the photograph in his hand; the rest was black crinkly ash on the floor of the shower and the water there was gradually drawing it out of its crinkly shape and into a black sludge.

Gone.

Whittaker glanced up and saw his own face in the mirror. The blood had run down from his temple to his neck and was like a blood-red waterfall. A little of it gathered about his collar, and he could feel that it would soon run down his neck.

He gulped.

He ran water in the basin, and then drew back; he couldn't bend his head. He took a bath-towel off the rail, draped it round his shoulder and then put his head beneath the shower. He turned on the cold water, gently at first; it spurted out more fiercely than he expected, and he winced and drew back, but in a moment he could stand it, and he felt the blood washing away. He backed away, raised the towel up round the left side of his face and dabbed until he felt that he was fairly dry. He looked at his reflection again.

It wasn't a bad job. There was still a red smear on his cheek and at his collar, but the river had gone, and the only real blood-red was at his collar. He dabbed again, then turned away from the mirror. He mustn't waste time. He went into the bedroom and winced at the sight of the girl's body as if he hadn't seen it before. There wasn't a thing he could do.

Wasn't there?

He could search the room.

He tried. Most drawers were empty, and Olive Johns had only three suitcases. He went through everything, but didn't find a thing. He couldn't make a real job of it. Soon he turned towards the door.

If he could get up to the other room without being seen, to room 71 . . .

No. That meant going upstairs and going downstairs, and he couldn't make such a journey. He wasn't sure that he was physically capable, for he knew that it wouldn't be long before he blacked out. He stood looking about him stupidly, and then someone came along the passage.

He felt like screaming.

A man and a woman, walking briskly, purposefully.

He stared at the door without moving.

They passed.

He put a hand to the uninjured side of his head, which seemed to be aching more than the other; as if blood had given some release from pain. He had to face it; he couldn't go upstairs and then down, and he wasn't much good on his

149

own. If he appeared at the elevator like this, he would have everybody screaming for an ambulance, and the police would be here before he could get to the swing doors. If he had ever needed help in his life he needed it now.

He moved heavily, reached the bedside table where the photograph had laid, and stared at the telephone. Then he picked it up. Almost at once a man answered.

'Desk clerk, help you?'

'Room 71, please,' Whittaker said and repeated, '71.'

'Right away.'

Whittaker heard the number being plugged; and then he was plagued by two doubts. Was it number 71? Was that the number Eve had given him? He couldn't be sure, not absolutely sure, now that he started to think about it. There was another thing: supposing she had gone? How long had he told her to wait? Half an hour? It was much longer than that, wasn't it, much longer than that?

Tck tck tck the plug went in and out.

'Sorry, can't get any reply,' the clerk said.

'All right,' muttered Whittaker. 'Thanks.' He put the receiver down slowly. He felt as if his world had come to an end, because he had so much to do, and it seemed more than he could manage. It was like relying on a boulder on a high mountain peak, putting one's whole weight on it, and then finding it give way.

Well, he'd have to manage by himself. The trouble was to get across the hall. If he went into the ill-lit restaurant he might have more chance; there would be that welcome dimness, and the soft-footed head-waiter, the bar, and the crooner. Yes, that was his best chance.

He turned towards the door.

It was opening.

*   *   *

Whittaker was half the length of the room away from the door, and he couldn't do a thing. He was incapable of swift action, now. His right arm hung limp and the strength had gone out of his body; a child couldn't have felt more useless, more helpless. He stood staring at the moving door. When he had slammed it in the face of the irate neighbour, it had latched, but he hadn't turned the key in the lock, and there was no way of stopping it from opening.

He had to take what came.

It opened wider, and he saw a woman's hand; and then Eve.

Eve.

He stood swaying, putting a hand out towards the wall, which was too far away for him to touch. *Eve.* He saw her face very clearly, saw the expression of alarm on it, the quick flash of dread. Then she came towards him. She didn't speak, but her right arm went about his waist, and suddenly he had someone to lean against. He didn't try to say a word; there was no need. To reach him, she had stepped over the girl's body, and he didn't think she had looked downwards after the first glance.

'Neil,' she said, when he was steady against her slender strength 'we've got to get to the car. I'll help you to the elevator, and we'll go from the elevator to the restaurant, because that's the quickest way. Now you've got to do it, do you understand?'

He nodded; and his head began to scream.

'If we had a hat,' she said, 'if only——' She broke off, with an exclamation, and he wondered what she had seen; and then, with the delayed action which he could do nothing about, he thought, *'The door.'*

It wasn't the door.

On a post at the foot of the bed was a hat; just a light-weight hat; the other man's.

'See that,' Whittaker said hoarsely. 'Hat.'

'Don't talk, Neil.'

'Hat.'

'Come on,' Eve said.

She didn't add that they should pray that no one chose to walk along the passage at this moment, or that no one came to their floor when they called the lift. Every second was going to hold its menace and its acute danger. He tried to brace himself. Eve's arm was still around him, and he thought vaguely that they must look funny. Then they began to walk.

The door.

The passage.

The corner.

The elevator.

It opened.

Whittaker felt his heart turn over and felt a shiver run through Eve's body. They stood still. The doors opened wide, and the elevator light was very bright. A shadow appeared, and then a man of middle-age, rounded and sleekly dressed, with a woman who was considerably younger. The woman averted her gaze but Whittaker hardly noticed that; he just noticed the couple who were within a few feet of him. They stepped out of the elevator and turned right, towards the room which Whittaker and Eve had left. The man had brushed close to Whittaker, his head within six inches of the ugly wound in Whittaker's temple.

'Step in,' said Eve steadily, and helped him.

The slight jolt of the lift as it started downwards threatened to lift Whittaker's head from his shoulders. He thought, foolishly, that he was much worse than he had thought. He wasn't so much worried as annoyed by that; he resented being helpless, even if he was being helped by Eve.

They stopped and the doors slid open.

No one was immediately in front of them, waiting to go up, and when Whittaker turned towards the restaurant, his wounded side was towards the wall. Two women in the corner might be puzzled because Eve was supporting him, the head-waiter might wonder why that was necessary, but— they wouldn't see the blood on his coat, would they?

'Would you like a cab, ma'am?' the head-waiter purred.

'No, thank you,' Eve said. 'The car's just along the street.'

Whittaker knew that the man opened the street door for them, and suspected that he stood and watched them, but he didn't care. His head seemed to be swelling. The pain in his right arm was getting worse now, because she kept knocking against it. He couldn't blame her, but there it was; every time they took a step it was as if someone had twisted his arm, and two broken ends of a bone grated.

They reached the corner.

He swayed helplessly.

'Neil,' Eve said desperately, 'you've got to keep on your feet until we get to the car. You've got to.'

'Feet,' he said. 'Hat. Feet, eh?'

'Come on,' she said, 'it's green.' She took a step and

152

seemed to be taking his arm with her. He groaned. He heard footsteps, but was not aware of the way people stared at them. He hardly realised that Eve was dragging him across the road towards the car.

CHAPTER XXI

FEAR

WHITTAKER was still conscious. He knew that he stood by the side of the car, and that Eve was speaking to him, but he didn't understand what she wanted him to do. It was as if he had lost complete control of his mind, as if nothing would signal from his brain to the rest of his body.

'Neil, step in—you must step in!'

He heard the edge of fear in Eve's voice, and could easily understand it. He wanted to help her to get rid of it, but that wasn't so easy. Then he realised that the door was opened.

'Help you, lady?' a man said.

Whittaker felt Eve's arm tighten round his waist. Thank God, she was on the other side now! His right arm wasn't hurting so much; it was painful, but not being twisted, not scraping and screaming at the same time. And now, someone else was here.'

'Help you, lady?' And Eve stiffened as if she were suddenly frightened.

It was a cop.

Eve said: 'Would you be that kind? I'm afraid I've had a little trouble with him.'

'Sure, I can see,' said the policeman bluffly. 'You ain't the only one to have that kind of man-trouble, lady. You go get in and help pull from the inside.'

'Thank you very much,' Eve said.

Pull?

In a panic Whittaker thought, '*Don't leave me!*' But she had gone. Instead of her firm arm, there was the massive arm of the policeman slapped round his waist like a band of steel. The policeman had no finesse at all, but treated Whittaker as he would a sack of corn leaning his weight against

153

him but hardly touching that right arm.

Eve called, 'All right, now!'

'Here he comes,' said the policeman.

Whittaker didn't know how the man did it, would probably never know. It was a combination of shoulder action, arm action, and leg action. One moment he was leaning heavily against the policeman, possessed by the despairing fear that he would never be put inside the car; the next, he was on the edge of the seat being pushed along, and something was grabbing at his left arm, pulling his arm.

'*No!*' he screamed.

The cop had withdrawn from the car. Eve, who had pulled his arm, dropped it as if it had burned her. Whittaker sat there with the pain sawing up and down, in his arm and head, knowing that he shouldn't have screamed, knowing that it might change the cop's whole outlook on the incident, knowing that he, Whittaker, couldn't do a thing about it. Sweat ran down his forehead and into his eyes, down his cheeks and into his mouth.

'Say, he sounds hurt,' the cop said.

'It's an old trouble,' Eve told him swiftly. 'He put his shoulder out playing football.'

Whittaker distinguished the words, without being able to tell whether they were convincing or not. He heard nothing else. He just sat there, oozing sweat, and feeling the pain and the waves which ran up and down his body. He couldn't take any more of it. They must stop, they must stop, he must rest, must . . .

There was vibration, movement, a jolting which made him gasp again, but he didn't scream this time. Good work. He didn't scream. He mustn't scream any more. Here he was sitting next to Eve in a car and being driven along—to where?

They went over a manhole, and jolted his arm.

He cried, 'No, no, no!' in a moaning kind of way.

He didn't see how Eve looked at him, he didn't see the lights, except those which were tinged with red; everything was because of the mists in his eyes. He felt the movement only because of the pain it brought; pain and fear. He didn't know what the fear was, at first, but something happened to make him understand.

It was fear of death.

No!

So this was how it came.

He found himself gritting his teeth, as he had often done since he stepped into stateroom *A14* and seen the back of Bob Gann's head. This was how it came, this was the process of dying. He had often faced it. His wife and now Eve had cried that he would go on until he let himself get killed, and that was what he had done. He could feel the coma creeping over him. He could feel a choking sensation in his throat and a tightness in his lungs. He remembered the sound which he had heard from Olive, and the sound he had made himself, when he had pretended.

He had mocked life then.

He had fought as if he could never die, but here was death coming to him, and he hated and feared it. Then, although it had in fact been close, it had seemed a million miles away. Now night was close upon him, like a cloud rolling over the mountains of the world towards him. And in his fear he fought against it with useless sweat and grunting and groaning and writhing.

He knew that the car stopped.

He knew that the door opened.

He did not know that five minutes passed between those two incidents, or that when the door opened Eve and her sister were together. Eve drew him out of the car, pulling his other arm now, and that didn't hurt. Then Rachel took his left side, and Eve went to the other. She hurt, but not so much as she had before; she knew what she was doing, now. They didn't have to go far; just to the elevator. He sensed that he was in it, and his head seemed to lift off when they started up, but there was nothing he could do about it.

He heard words.

Morphia—doctor—hospital—bed. All of these were jumbled up in his mind, and they were all meaningless, because he was sure that he was going to die. He still feared that; he had never known anything like the fear. It seemed to him that there was a yawning gap in the life he knew, that it was too wide to span, and that in trying to get to the other side he would have to drop into death.

He writhed.

He sweated.

He felt coolness upon his arms, and then a sharp prick in

155

one arm, and he didn't quite know what it was—but he did know he was going to die. He could feel death creeping over him, in waves. Those billowing clouds were coming down the mountain; he couldn't get out of their way. He wanted to shriek and to turn and run; he wanted to do anything except wait and let them bring their darkness, but he couldn't move. He was being held down, someone was pressing against him harder and harder.

He screamed.

He felt the clouds about him now, in his mind, in his heart.

This was death.

He couldn't resist it any longer.

*   *   *

Eve stood away from the bed where Whittaker lay, and put a hand to her damp and quivering lips. Her sister, calmer than she, was moving away from the bed. She went out of the room, and Eve stood looking down on Whittaker's desperately pale face, on the closed eyes, on the ugly wound in the temple. He seemed hardly to be breathing, but she knew that he was alive. The morphia had brought him relief from pain, but had also given him the fear which his final convulsive shout had revealed. She knew what he feared; it was as if death stretched out and touched her also.

Rachel came back.

She didn't speak, but moved nearer to Whittaker, and put a damp towel lightly on his forehead, then wiped his glistening cheeks and lips; next she put a wet cloth between his lips. He was just breathing. She stood back from the bed and said quietly:

'Eve, don't just stand there.'

Eve didn't move or speak.

'I've telephoned for Dr. Clister,' Rachel said. 'He'll be here in twenty minutes. He's the only one we can rely on not to go running to the police. You know that. Now, relax, Eve; you've done all you can.'

Eve said: 'I told him not to go. I did everything in the world to stop him, and he wouldn't listen. He just wouldn't listen to me; he——'

'*Eve!*'

Eve turned away slowly.

'All right,' she said in a dull and empty voice, 'I know, I'm being foolish; I'm sorry, Rachel.' She moved away from the bed, and seemed as if she would blunder into the open door. Her sister moved a hand to guide her. 'Somehow, it was as if I were looking at Bob, and not at a stranger. It's as if Bob were dying.'

'He's not dying,' Rachel said.

Eve raised her hands. 'Don't just say that.'

'I'm not just saying it! I believe it.'

'You—you don't think he'll die?'

'I don't think he'll die,' Rachel declared firmly. 'Eve, you must go and sit down. I've never seen you anything like this. If you go on this way, you'll have a collapse, and then I'll have the two of you on my hands. Come on, let me give you a drink, and you'll feel better.'

She led the way into the living-room.

'After all,' she said practically, 'he isn't Bob. It's no use taking on so.'

'No,' said Eve. 'He's not Bob. Bob's dead, and Neil's going to die. Of course, he's going to die.'

Rachel was in a corner, pouring out brandy. She brought the glass across, and held it to her sister's lips. Eve sipped. She hardly noticed what she was drinking, and she looked blankly past Rachel. Neither spoke. Close together like that, the likeness between them was quite remarkable; had Rachel been a little taller, a little deeper-breasted, they would have looked identical.

'If you're so worried,' said Rachel, 'why don't you call a hospital?'

Eve said: 'I can't do that; you know I can't. The girl was dead; there was no evidence that anyone else had been in the room. *I* know—but add it all up, Rachel—add everything up. What could save him? Even if he were an undercover man for Scotland Yard it wouldn't help, not after all that's happened. At heart, Neil knows it; he always knew it, and yet he took the chances he did because he'd met Bob, and——'

Rachel said, 'Or because he'd met you.'

'No,' said Eve in a low voice. 'No, it wasn't that; it was something deeper, finer.'

'He's a man,' Rachel said.

157

Eve moved towards the window, pulled the cord at the side and opened the Venetian blinds so that she could look into the street. No cars came near. No shadowy figures lurked. The only movement was in the distance, on the Parkway and on the River.

'How long did Dr. Clister say he'd be?'

'He won't be long.'

'Rachel,' Eve said, 'if he dies I don't know what I shall do. I just don't know. It's as if——'

'Why don't you pull yourself together?' Rachel demanded roughly. She came striding across, and actually pulled at her sister's arm to make her turn round. 'You've just got to do that, Eve. Can't you understand what's happened? You've projected Bob's personality on to this man Whittaker. He isn't Bob, but you see him as Bob. When you heard that Bob had died you didn't believe it. Oh, you did with your mind and your reason, you knew it was true, and you've seen him lying in a morgue, but your heart rebelled. It was something you'd always feared, but it couldn't *really* happen. That's what you told yourself subconsciously, and —that's why you feel like this. Whittaker is Bob to you— but he *isn't* Bob. He's a complete stranger. He comes from a different country, from a different world. If you'd met him with Bob, you wouldn't have thought twice about him, he would be just another man. Now he's a sort of personification of Bob, almost a *deification*. You're coming near to worshipping him; it—it's hideous, I can't stand by and let it happen. *He's not Bob.*'

Eve just looked at her, with her eyes glinting as if silver had been poured into them.

'Eve,' Rachel cried, 'don't look like that!' She took her arm and shook her. 'I know what will happen if he dies. You will do just what you were doing before. You'll go home. You'll live with young Bob and Mimi. You'll live the life you've always lived. Bob's only been home for a few weeks here, a little time there, just a series of vacations, and you know it. You won't be looking forward to his coming home; that's the only difference. You'll be wholly self-sufficient, and you'll know it—you've not realised it before. Bob was a dream, a hero, someone you saw in your mind, and he was never home long enough to destroy the illusion. *That's the truth, Eve—why don't you see it?* His dying

158

won't make much difference to you, not really, not in living day by day. He's dead. Make yourself think that he's having a longer vacation, he——'

'Rachel,' Eve said, 'I don't want to talk about it any more. I just don't want to talk.' She peered out into the street, and a car turned the corner and came speeding. 'There's a car. It—it's slowing down. It's stopping. *Rachel!*'

CHAPTER XXII

HOPE

THE doctor was a tall, grave-faced man with grey hair and dark skin; skin so dark that in some lights it was almost black. His full lips were pursed as he examined Whittaker, and for a long time he did not speak. Then, his dark hands, with the pale filbert-shaped nails explored the wounds, very gently, cautiously. They looked jet-black against Whittaker's pale skin.

Eve watched.

Rachel, waited, as a nurse.

The doctor moved away from the bed and said:

'He should be taken to hospital, of course, and it can be arranged quickly.'

'No!' Eve exclaimed. 'No, he must stay here.'

The doctor looked at her gravely, hands raised and spread a little, stethoscope hanging round his thick neck. He wore a dark grey suit with the coat buttoned in spite of the warmth of the night. He had something of the look of Sister Joanna.

'My sister is very anxious that he shouldn't have to be questioned,' Rachel said. 'If you can help him here, please.'

'Yes,' said the doctor, 'I can help him. But there is much risk, Miss Rachel. If he should die, then . . .' he shrugged his shoulders and spread his hands. 'I am the doctor; I will be blamed. Is the reason great enough for that?' His gaze was on Rachel, not on Eve.

She didn't answer.

'Can you wait?' Eve asked desperately. '*Can't* you wait to see how he is in the morning? Can't you?'

159

Rachel said slowly: 'It could be an error of judgment, if anything goes wrong, couldn't it? You thought that he would be all right until morning, or until tomorrow night.'

The room was very quiet.

Whittaker lay still, pale as death.

'Yes,' said the doctor, 'it could be an error of judgment. But you forget that there is more than that—a man's life might be at stake. If he stays here he may possibly die: if he is moved to hospital for X-ray and thorough examination, I feel sure that he can be saved. Is it worth taking such a risk, Miss Rachel?'

Rachel turned.

'Is it, Eve?'

'Yes,' said Eve. She spoke stiffly, as if the word had to be forced out. 'Yes,' she repeated, 'he would think so. Please do all you can for him, here.'

The doctor bowed.

'I shall need a nurse, Miss Rachel,' he said, quietly, 'and this room must be turned into a theatre. It can be said that I believed it would be fatal to move him. Yes, it can be said,' he repeated, and he seemed easier in his mind. 'I would like to use the telephone.'

Rachel turned and led the way.

* * *

There were mists.

Whittaker did not remember where he had seen them before; did not recall that he had pictured them as coming over the peaks of high mountains, to roll down and engulf him as if they were choking the life out of him. All he knew was that there was mist, and he could not see. It was as if his head was filled with it, and the room he was in. He did not think consciously about it, or about anything else; he was just aware of it, as one would be aware of clouds on a high mountain.

* * *

There was pale light.

Whittaker knew that it was a light which he had seen before, and which was important to him. . . . A distant, silvery light, like that of dawn at the moment of a fine day.

It was very clear. He did not feel pain, and he could not see, but he knew that he was awake, and alive.

*   *   *

There were shadows, which moved against the light, shapes which he could see, without realising that they were there. There were sounds, too, of voices pitched on a low key. He knew that people were in the room with him. He was not aware of pain, and yet he was aware of strangeness, in his left arm, and on the right side of his head; as if he had neither left arm nor right temple. That was really the beginning of recollection, the beginning of new hope. He had not consciously thought he was dead, but there had been that vivid feeling of dying before he had lost consciousness. Now, he knew that he was alive, and sensed exhilaration and the hope that he would stay alive. He was comparatively free from fears; those he had were of nebulous things, not of men like Ricky's boys, or of women like Olive, or of photographs. He lay in a semi-conscious state for a long time, gradually remembering, and most vivid of all was his memory of Eve.

*   *   *

'Yes,' said Eve, 'you're still here, at Rachel's apartment, and you can stay here for as long as you like.'

Whittaker looked at her.

The blinds were drawn so that hardly any daylight came in, and he couldn't see her clearly, but he didn't forget a single feature of her face. Her voice was subdued, too, and calm. He remembered how he had felt panic when the policeman had helped him into the car, and he remembered everything that she had done for him.

He said, 'How long have I been here?'

'Five days.'

'Five *days*?'

'And you can stay five weeks or five months.'

He didn't answer. It shocked him to think that there was a gap in his mind of five whole days. He did not want to stir himself too much, or to grapple with the significance of that, but—five *days*.

'Has anything—happened?'

161

'Nothing you need worry about. I had to let Pirran go, but that was all. I've not been threatened; there's been no trouble.'

'The police? Have they——?'

'They haven't been here. Why should they come here?'

'What about—the Lamprey?'

'Neil,' Eve said firmly, 'it isn't going to help you if you start agitating yourself. You've got to forget all that, and get well. The doctor thinks he can get you on your feet again in another ten days if you'll do everything he tells you, and one of those orders is—don't worry.' She stood up. 'I mustn't stay any longer. Is there anything you want?'

He didn't answer.

'Is there anything you want?'

Whittaker knew that he was frowning. He couldn't help it, because of the effort of memory. He stared at her, wishing he could see her face more clearly, and yet for the moment that wasn't the most important thing.

'The—the packet of diamonds?' he said huskily.

'Don't think of it, don't harass yourself about it!'

'Is it found?'

'No,' she said.

*　　　*　　　*

Whittaker looked about the empty room. The Venetian blinds were open slightly, so that the sun could shine between the slats and make patterns on the carpet and on the legs of chairs which stood in the way. He could hear the noises of the street. He knew that the room had become part of his life, and that in some ways it was the most important part. Eve, quiet-voiced and quiet-moving, Rachel with the same kind of grace and quietness, had been his only companions, except for the tall, handsome coloured doctor, with his assurances and his slight hint of anxiety, as if his gravity were caused by something more than his knowledge of the patient's health.

He had been awake for half an hour.

His head felt quite clear again, and there was no suspicion of an ache in it—nor in his arm. His arm was in a plaster cast, of course: the chair had broken it. But he was assured that it would mend, and that in a short while he would hardly know that it had been seriously damaged. There was nothing to worry about there. The head wound was healing, too, and he had recovered much of the lost blood. There was no danger left: all he had to do was to take things quietly, when he was up and about again. Eve had talked about a cabin she had in the Adirondacks, somewhere near Lake Placid, but they had not gone into that seriously.

He wondered when she would come. He wanted to see her, although he knew that when she came there was a risk that they would clash again.

He wanted to know about—everything.

All he knew was that there was no news about the diamonds, as far as Eve was aware. No arrests had been made. The news of the murder of Olive Johns had screeched from the front pages for a day, and since then other crimes and other sensations had driven her story to small paragraphs. He had seen some of these and they meant less than nothing. He knew that the *Queen B.* had been back to England, had been here again and was halfway across the Atlantic by now.

He knew that when Eve released Pirran, Pirran had gone off; he didn't know where.

As far as he knew, nothing had happened to Ricky, Blick, or Moyan; nothing that the newspapers had reported, anyhow.

He kept thinking of Olive Johns and her story; her talk of having given the packet to this veiled woman whom she couldn't identify. Who had been to the Lamprey Hotel, to take the packet? Who . . .

He must find Pirran again, or get to Ricky. There was something to puzzle out. Once he had been knocked out and Olive dead, the trouble had stopped: Eve hadn't been in any further danger. All had been quiet. Did that mean that Ricky had found the packet? Was it all over? Had Olive said something that had given Blick a vital clue?

If she had, what could it be?

Just the diamonds had been given to a woman whom Bob Gann had known?

* * *

If it was someone whom Bob Gann had known, then it could be Rachel.

* * *

Whittaker was alone in the apartment for the first time. He wasn't well, but he was much better. He knew exactly what he wanted to do, and he knew also that this was next to Rachel's room. He'd seen hers, and he knew that this had once been a dressing-room. It was at the back of the building, too, and quieter than the larger rooms at the front.

For the first time Whittaker got out of bed unaided. He wasn't steady on his feet, but he kept upright. He went into the big bright room beyond, with its large bed, its silks, its colours; and he reached a writing-bureau. He sat at it, breathing heavily, until he felt he could screw himself up to further effort. It had a flap which, when lowered, made a level surface for writing; but it was locked.

Soon, he picked at the lock.

In five minutes he had it open.

He rummaged through the papers, found nothing which offered any evidence; nothing which even hinted at it. He kept on, tapping the sides and the roof and the base of the recess in the bureau.

Then he found the tiny indentation, only large enough for a finger-nail. He pressed and discovered what he wanted; the false compartment.

There it lay.

He stared at the packet unbelievingly. It answered the description: a sealed, brown paper packet. He felt quite sure what it was, and yet didn't really believe it. *Here.*

He forgot everything, until——

He heard a key in the front door.

For a moment he was in a sweat of utter panic. Physical weakness made it worse, and he could hardly think, he couldn't move. Then the door opened and closed, and Eve called out:

'I'm back, Rachel!'

Whittaker put the packet back, then pushed the lever, and the compartment fell into position, but—it wasn't locked. He had time, he must have time.

'*Rachel!* Are you there?'

Eve was nearer.

Whittaker closed the drawer and moved away. He hardly knew how he got to his bedroom without falling. He reached the bed and collapsed before getting in. His whole body was wet with sweat, and for all he knew Eve was already in the room, looking at him.

If she were she didn't speak to him.

Somehow, he got into bed. The plaster cast made difficulties and his weak legs made more; the springs creaked; but he got there and lay down.

Bob's accomplice was Rachel.

Eve. . . .

Eve *mustn't* know. She was in the other room, he realised, and hadn't come in here. He could still hear her in there.

What was she doing?

*   *   *

Whittaker was still weak from the exertions. Drugs had kept his nerves quiet for a long time, but he had done much more than he should, and could not regain full self-control. He listened intently, sure that Eve hadn't come into this room, but puzzled by the quiet and by the fact that she hadn't come to see him.

He still heard movement in Rachel's room—the room where he'd been, where *it* was.

It was repeated.

What was Eve doing there?

Eve in Rachel's room.

The sound came again; and somehow it seemed furtive. Was that his imagination? Had the need for swift escape, added to the shock of the discovery, made him imagine . . .

There was a subdued kind of thud, then tapping as of fingers on wood, and—after a long pause—a squeak.

He had heard that squeak when lifting the lid of the bureau. What was *Eve* doing?

Squeak.

Whittaker eased himself up on his elbow, and that in itself cost considerable effort. He shouldn't do it; he hadn't recovered enough. He felt clumsy and fearful in case he taxed himself too much. He tried to peer through the partly-open door, but couldn't see anything except the carpet and the foot of a chair or a table.

Tap—tap—tap.

What was Eve doing?

Did she suspect that Rachel and Bob . . .

He had to find out; and there was only one way; to get

165

up again. The thought was agony in itself, but it had to be done.

His heart was banging.

He pushed back the bedclothes and fought against the nausea which the thought of the effort brought on. He beat it. The bedclothes were back at last, and he could put one leg over the side of the bed and grope for the floor.

Tap—tap——

Then he heard a stifled exclamation and had no doubt what it meant. Eve had found the secret panel; she was staring down at the packet as he had done.

Then he heard another sound, a fearful one, because it was so utterly unexpected.

Another key in the front door!

He caught his breath.

This would be Rachel, and Rachel would go straight into the room next door, would find Eve at the writing-bureau.

There was a flurry of sound in the room next door, as if Eve were in a desperate hurry as he had been. What could he do to help her?

Rachel, from the hallway, called clearly, 'Where are you, Eve?'

There was no answer, just the flurry of movement in Rachel's room. Only he could help Eve now; if he could attract Rachel's attention, calling out, and bring her straight in here——

He hadn't raised his voice for weeks.

'Rachel! Come—come and help, come!'

He stopped abruptly.

The communicating door opened wider, and Eve appeared: a frightened Eve, her face red, her eyes strangely bright, as if by burning. She held the packet in her hand—the one he had seen. *It*.

'Neil, be quiet——' she began.

'*Eve!*' exclaimed Rachel.

There was another flurry of sound as she drew within Whittaker's line of vision. Eve turned round. The two sisters faced each other, with Eve holding the packet and Rachel holding a gun.

166

THE PACKET

EVE had her back to Whittaker, and he could just see Rachel over her shoulder, and at her side. By her side, Rachel held the gun. It was a small automatic, probably .22; as deadly as a revolver in the right hands. She wore a hat and a linen suit; Eve had on a dress of powder blue.

It was hard to believe that there could be such silence and such lack of movement.

Whittaker, still on his elbow, and with one foot out of the bed and pointing towards the floor, had to move one way or the other, his arm wouldn't stand him. He eased himself upwards, to a sitting position, and then sat up in the bed. Now, he could hear the breathing of the two sisters. He wished above all things that he could see Eve's face, but he could not.

Rachel spoke.

'Neil,' she said, 'don't get out of bed.' Another silence followed before she went on: 'So you guessed, Eve. How did you guess?'

Eve didn't answer.

'Why don't you tell me?' Rachel asked. 'In the long run, it won't make any difference. How did you guess?'

Eve said quietly: 'I didn't just guess, Rachel. Neil talked a lot in his sleep. When he was in a fever, too. He kept saying it was a woman who knew Bob. I couldn't make it out at first, but gradually I began to understand. Bob knew about the diamonds and had played some part in all of this. It was hard to face,' Eve went on in a remote voice. 'But I had to face it. I had to think. I went over all his friends, all the women he knew. And then the police questioned me.'

Rachel caught her breath.

'They asked me to call on them,' Eve said evenly, 'and when I arrived there was a man with them—one of Ricky's men, named Blick. Blick had talked; Blick had killed Olive Johns, and had told them all she said to him. They told me this,' Eve continued, as if each word hurt; then, 'So I knew a great deal.

'Then, last night, when you were out, a man telephoned. He asked for you. Something in his manner made me wonder what he really wanted, and I pretended to be you.

'He said, "If you don't bring those diamonds, you're as good as dead." That was enough. I had to search, and find out if the diamonds were here.'

She stopped.

'It's a great pity you pretended to be me,' Rachel said, after a long pause; 'it would have been much better if you'd never known.'

Eve said, 'But now I know.'

Whittaker wished that she would turn round, longed to see her; that was more important than what he heard them say, although this was the end of the story.

She didn't turn round.

'I don't understand,' Eve went on, and she spoke slowly, as if she were truly baffled. 'I just don't understand it, Rachel. Why should Bob work with you? Had you been associates for—for long?' A long silence. 'Didn't I give him everything? . . . *everything?*'

'Yes,' said Rachel. 'You gave him too much.'

'Too *much?*' Eve's voice seemed strangled.

'In giving, you wanted too much,' said Rachel carefully. 'He wasn't a generous giver. You should have found that out. He couldn't give all of himself. I knew what you didn't know, Eve. I should have let him do anything to me but not betray you, but I hadn't the strength. I don't think he loved me; I think if he loved anyone it was you.'

Eve said emptily: 'Yes. But why—why should he betray his work, why——?'

'He couldn't resist temptation any longer,' Rachel said. 'So he took his big chance. I was glad to help him. I loved him quite as much as you ever did.'

Eve moved at last, backing into the room. The hand with the packet was stretched out behind her, but she wasn't trying to get rid of it; she was groping for somewhere to sit down, or to rest again. Whittaker didn't speak to offer guidance, for she touched a chair and then sat down on it, her profile towards him. Rachel came further into the room; and in a way the situation was worse than it had been, because with the gun she could cover both Whittaker and Eve.

She held the gun loosely as she said: 'I wish I hadn't got to tell you, but you've got to understand. You've *got* to understand, Eve. When Bob went to Europe this time he was after these diamonds. That was his real job. He and I made a deal. He'd get them, but it would look as if Ricky had taken them, and Bob would be in the clear. We were going to share equally. I would be able to spend money on projects like Joanna's church. God, how I've longed to do that! At least, the money would do good.' For a moment Rachel paused with a catch in her breath. But she didn't close her eyes, and the hand holding the gun was very still. She could raise it in a flash, towards either or both of them. 'You've got to admit that, Eve.'

Eve said thinly: 'Yes. Yes, I suppose it would.'

'You suppose, you . . .' Rachel began, and for the first time she raised her voice; but the shrillness didn't last, and she broke off abruptly. Then, 'It's no use shouting at each other,' she said. 'At least we can be civilised.'

Eve seemed to echo the word, for her lips moved; but she didn't make any sound.

'After the murders I hoped it would all die down,' Rachel went on. 'When Olive died I thought it was nearly over. Just a few more weeks and I could start selling some of the diamonds. Bob had told me whom he'd go to. I was all set. But it hasn't worked out. Ricky guesses I have them. He once thought Bob had sent them to you, and sent a man to frighten you. Remember when you were nearly shot at, and your new hero saved you? Ricky was going to soften you up. Well, he didn't. He switched to me, and I don't know whether I can beat him or not. But—I'm going to *try*.' Her voice grew harsh, bitter. 'I was going to switch him on to Whittaker. You'll admit that I *tried* to help Whittaker; I took big risks in having him attended here. I used my influence with Dr. Clister, and Sister Joanna, who sent the nurse when a nurse was needed. I believed that when he was well again, I could make Ricky think that Whittaker had the diamonds. It was worth trying, Stalling, playing for time, trying. And—I'm *going* to try!'

'You'll never do it,' said Eve huskily.

'Then we'll all lose,' Rachel said, 'but I'm going to try. I'm going to kill you both. Then I'm going to send for Ricky, and promise him a deal. And when he's here, I'll send for the police. He'll be so tightly framed he won't have a chance to get out. And between killing you and sending

169

for him, I'll have put the diamonds away.'

She stopped, breathing very hard, as if she hated herself for what she was planning.

'Rachel,' Eve said in a stronger voice, 'what makes you think of killing me? What is it?'

'Simply to get the money for all the things I've always wanted to do—all the good it will bring. I can't give it up— I just can't.'

Eve didn't speak again.

'I tell you I can't give it up!' Rachel screamed, and raised her free hand. 'I tell you I can't! Don't look at me like that: don't!' She raised the gun, and Whittaker felt his heart bound, and made an effort to fling himself forward. He could not, had no chance at all to help the woman he loved. 'Why should I, why——'

'Rachel, my dear,' said a man from behind her, 'you should give them up because they don't belong to you. They belong to us all.'

She spun round.

A man out of sight of Whittaker fired at her. Her gun was twisted from her wrist, and she backed away, as if she could not believe her eyes.

Pirran came in sight, holding a gun.

*   *   *

Men, outside, came running.

Pirran was smiling, in a funny little deprecating way.

'They belong to the Government, Rachel, that's what I mean. I serve the Government. Oddly, perhaps, but loyally. I had the task of finding the diamonds, and I found them. The mistakes I made came later.' He spoke very quietly and confidently. 'I wasn't sure of Whittaker, and I wasn't sure of Bob Gann. I had to check them both, and when Camponi ran amok, I was back where I started. I played it the way I thought best—and at least it's worked out.' A smile made the corners of his lips droop in a droll way. 'It's all right, Whittaker, I hold no grudge. You in your way and I in mine, we did what we believed we had to do. In fact I have been very proud to know you.'

Men were filling the room beyond, now; some uniformed police and some in plain-clothes.

'I followed you in today, using a key which I had made

170

many weeks ago,' Pirran said to Rachel. 'Some of your friends in Harlem told me that you were showing an interest in the jewel merchants there. Loyalty is a strange thing, Rachel. Loyalty to the country goes very deep in unsuspected people, and is shallow with the most unlikely ones, too. But that is a truism. You were allowed to keep Whittaker here. You have been closely watched, because, you see, we had reason to suspect Bob. We knew of his association with you. We didn't know whether his wife was involved in this deal, and didn't know whether we could really trust Whittaker. But Dr. Clister told us that Whittaker would soon be about again; we guessed you were trying to find a market for the diamonds. So it was time we moved in.

'Don't run away, Rachel.'

'Don't——'

She turned and ran, past Whittaker, past Eve, towards the passage, across it, with men thundering after her. Her footsteps clattered on the kitchen floor. A man shouted. There was a crash of glass, and a man shouted in horror:

'*Stop her! She's jumping out!*'

There was no time to stop her.

*　　*　　*

Pirran came back to the room a few minutes afterwards, and Whittaker watched and waited. Eve was by the window; and in these few quivering minutes no one could help her to fight her battle.

Neither of them tried.

Whittaker had to say something, could not just look at her. 'So you were an F.B.I. man, Gus?' He spoke flatly, wearily. 'You were in danger first, and then the danger faded when you did the deal with Maisie. But Camponi found out.'

Pirran smiled very faintly.

'I can tell you most of the story now,' he said. 'How Camponi discovered that I was bribing Maisie, and . . .'

He seemed as anxious as Whittaker to talk; perhaps believing that it might help Eve, or at least stop her from thinking those tormenting thoughts. As Pirran talked, the pieces fell into place. Most of it Whittaker already knew, but he had never heard the whole story before in a coherent whole.

171

Ricky sent Camponi to Europe for the diamond theft. The F.B.I. sent Pirran and Bob—Bob not knowing who Pirran was. Pirran stole the diamonds back, deliberately taking the risk so as to draw not only Camponi but the great Ricky.

There he failed.

Camponi killed in that awful night at sea, Bob, waiting his chance, got the diamonds and gave them to Olive—on the afternoon of the murders.

Bob died.

Maisie died.

Olive escaped and did a courageous best, and nearly succeeded, but Ricky suspected her and kept at her, until Blick killed her: an accidental murder.

Then Rachel had the jewels.

There wasn't much more that anyone needed to be reminded of. Now, Whittaker knew it all, except . . .

'What about Ricky?' he asked gruffly.

'We're going to hang Ricky,' Pirran said dreamily. 'Blick talked, and he has the evidence we need.' Pirran looked at Eve, and added very quietly: 'Bob always said he would get Ricky one day. Remember?'

Eve didn't speak; could only turn away.

* * *

Two hours later, in the apartment, Pirran and the Government officials opened the packet and displayed the shimmering beauty of a million dollars' worth of diamonds.

'Payment from European Governments for goods they needed desperately,' Pirran said. He gave his almost droll, fish-like smile. 'Tell me, Whittaker, did I fool you or did you begin to suspect who I was? Is that why you let me go?'

'You fooled me utterly,' Whittaker admitted. He didn't smile. 'Now fool me again, will you? In your position I would question Mrs. Gann at once; I would break her down until she told me everything she knew—although she may not know a thing. Fool me, Pirran. Leave her alone, and leave us here, will you?'

Pirran said, 'If at any time either of you needs help, I hope you will let me know.'

He went out.

Eve was still sitting in the chair where she had been when Rachel had made the move to shoot her.

Whittaker moved slowly as he heard the outside door close. He would move clumsily for a long time. He would probably do and say the wrong thing for a long time. He was in no position to tell Eve what he felt, to say how precious she was to him. He could not even begin to tell her that he understood how deep the wound had gone. He could only hope that before long she would begin to live again, first for the children and then for herself—and later, perhaps, for him.

He got off the bed and stood there weak on his legs; he hadn't really walked unaided yet.

He took a step forward.

'Eve,' he said in a husky voice, 'I need—I need your help.'

She turned her face slowly and blindly towards him; as if she could not see; and he wondered if she would ever be able to see life clearly again. For that moment, despair clutched at him. But it loosed its hold, for she saw him, and in a swift movement, got up and came towards him, saying:

'You mustn't do that! Neil, you must get well quickly.' She reached him. 'You must, do you understand, you must get well.'

'It's all right,' Whittaker said, and he thought of Pirran as he spoke of himself. 'In fact, it's fine, Eve. I'm the man who *didn't* die.' He put his arm about her shoulders as she helped him on to the bed. 'Because you wouldn't let me' he went on. 'There isn't another reason in the world.'

THE END

CALL FOR THE BARON

by JOHN CREASEY

writing as Anthony Morton, creator of The Baron

A series of minor thefts at Vere House prompts Martin and Diana Vere to call in their old friend John Mannering to investigate. But while Mannering is doing so, the jewels and the famous Deverall necklace belonging to Lady Usk, a guest of the Vere's are stolen. Reluctantly, the police are brought in and much to Mannering's disquiet, Scotland Yard send their top man, Chief Inspector Bristow, one of the few who suspect Mannering to be the Baron—the cleverest jewel thief in the country.

And Mannering realises it is even more imperative that he prove his innocence when he discovers someone has planted the stolen Deverall necklace in his room . . .

552 09297 5—**30p**   T146

YOU FIND HIM—I'LL FIX HIM

by JAMES HADLEY CHASE

Helen Chalmers had the kind of figure which could make a man do almost anything she wanted. So when she asked Ed Dawson to spend a month alone with her in a secluded Italian villa, he found himself accepting—even though it was against his better judgement.

His judgement told him he was crazy—that involvement with Helen would mean trouble as her father, apart from being one of the richest and most influential men in the world, was also his employer. He wouldn't take too kindly to his daughter being compromised by one of his employees. What Ed's judgement didn't tell him was that upon his arrival at the villa he would find Helen lying dead at the bottom of a cliff, and a strange man searching through the rooms with a flashlight . . .

0 552 09603 2—**35p**   T210

LAY HER AMONG THE LILIES
by JAMES HADLEY CHASE

It was odd that a healthy young heiress like Janet Crosby should die of heart failure. Odder still, that on the day she died she sent a note and $500 to Vic Malloy, private investigator, asking him to trace the person who was blackmailing her sister.

Intrigued by the note, Malloy tried to see Maureen Crosby but only got as far as her nurse—a curvaceous blonde with an engaging bedside manner. Next he tried to see Janet's personal maid, but found that somebody else had reached her first and made sure that she wouldn't talk to anyone—ever again . . .

552 09551 6—35p   T170

I WOULD RATHER STAY POOR
by JAMES HADLEY CHASE

Like most bank managers, Dave Calvin had acquired an irresistible charm that he could switch on whenever he felt the necessity. Underneath it he was cold, calculating, brutal —a perfect murderer . . .

For years he waited—watching an endless stream of money pass through his hands—knowing that a risk was only worth taking if the reward was justified. And a three hundred thousand dollar payroll was justification enough—even for murder . . .

552 09491 9—35p   T171

A SELECTED LIST OF CRIME STORIES
FOR YOUR READING PLEASURE